Threshing Days

A Story of Farming in the North Riding

William. R. Alderson

Threshing Days

A Story of Farming in the North Riding

William. R. Alderson

Japonica Press

First Published 2011

ISBN: 978-1-904686-22-4

A catalogue record for this book is available from the British Library

Published by
Japonica Press
Low Green Farm, Hutton, Driffield,
East Yorkshire, YO25 9PX
United Kingdom

Acknowledgements

People who have helped with photographs or help in any other way to whom I am indebted.

Alf Alderson
Leslie Atkinson
Beamish Museum
Elsie Banks
Angela Duffus
Mabel Beacon
Ian Gibson
Dick Lovelace
The Northern Echo
Richard Preston
Preston Hall Museum
David Robinson
Jimmy Sedgewick
Ann Smith
David Stainthorpe
Jane Strickland
Alex Turnbull
Linda Tweddle
Michael & Joan Walker
Les Walker
Alistair Wilkin
Gladys Woodhead

In addition to these I would like to thank my long suffering family including:

Mother - Mrs Molly Anderson for photographs and reminiscences
Sister - Mrs Elizabeth Robinson for the back cover piece
Daughter - Anne Alderson for her work whith this computer
Grand daughter - Jemma Alderson for her work with the photographs

To anybody not included above who feels they have contributed in any way accept my apologies for the omission.

Contents

Acknowledgements   7

Introduction   11

Chapter 1   Early Life   14

Chapter 2   Threshing Tractors and Machinery   20

Chapter 3   The Harvest   40

Chapter 4   Threshing Days   58

Chapter 5   Steam Days   80

Chapter 6   The Manufacturers   88

Chapter 7   Threshers on the Road   102

Chapter 8   Threshing Day Meals   114

Chapter 9   The Last Day   124

William Oswald Alderson 1919 - 1992 threshing machine proprietor at 30 years of age.

Introduction

It is now over forty years since threshers stopped for the last time, and those of us who were there and were involved with threshing are becoming fewer in number. Those threshing machines that have survived to the present day are passing into the hands of younger men who never saw their actual operation. I am full of admiration for these younger people who are prepared to take on the not inconsiderable task of restoring and preserving a threshing machine. However, I feel that it would add to their enjoyment of the hobby if they had the benefit of the knowledge of some of those who took part in this work.

Pulling a machine alongside a trailer-load of sheaves on a warm Sunday afternoon in the twenty-first century is a world away from turning up to do a day's work at seven on a dark frosty morning, with the sheet ropes all frozen stiff. It is to try and bridge that gap that this book has come to fruition. It includes a description of the workings of the machine, how a threshing day was set out, and some reminiscences and amusing anecdotes of what went on.

This book is dedicated to the memory of my late father, William Oswald Alderson (WO). He began threshing in 1941 and it would be fair to say that his start in contracting was helped by the compulsory ploughing campaign of the Second World War. His early contracting was centred on ploughing and corn cutting, and, of course, threshing. His meticulous diary keeping not only records who the customer was but also which men did it and which tractor and equipment were used. These diaries are all intact and have been an inestimable help in the writing of this book. One of my earliest memories of my father was sitting close to the Tilley lamp with tweezers, extracting thistles from his hands picked up from a day feeding a crop that had been full of them.

I would also like to pay tribute to the men who worked for us. They were engaged primarily for threshing, but all were prepared to turn their hands to other work. There had been several men employed, many on a part-time basis, during the 1940s and into the early 1950s. From 1951 until 1957, we had the services of Les Harker, a young, fit chap who principally drove the Field Marshall and the threshing set with a baler. He was from a farming background and could do all other work when asked, including from 1955 driving a Massey Harris 780 combine. From the mid 1950s we employed two brothers, Eddie and Walter Robson, who served as feeder men to both sets. Usually, Walter worked with Les and Eddie, with WO. Both could do other work, which included land work, and in summer they both operated pick-up balers. In the early 1960s, they switched onto land drainage work and stayed with us until 1970. In the years 1952 to 1955, a father and son – Ernie and Chris Kirby – worked on a part-time basis. They took the third threshing set with a Fordson Major, and did a considerable amount of hay baling with a stationary baler. During the 1960s, as threshing became a part-time occupation and I took the job over myself, I had the services of George Helme. He had a small farm, milked twenty cows by hand before coming to thresh, and was able to find other work on farms as threshing became sparser.

The area covered by the stories in this book is south of the river Tees, from Yarm in the east to Croft in the west, and as far south as Great Smeaton, Appleton Wiske and Picton. We had built up a very compact 'round', largely within a 5-mile radius of home, and within that area we would do ninety-five per cent of the threshing. We did have one or two customers outside that area, including some over the river in County Durham. Much of the dialogue used reflects our northern dialect, and I have tried to include this when retelling some of the stories. The intention is to try and relay to the reader some of the atmosphere that was in evidence when ten or twelve men worked together, often under strenuous conditions.

There are many regional variations for the names of machines and their parts – too many to list fully – but the key ones are as follows: the threshing machine was known in Eastern England as 'the drum'; some knew it as 'the threshing box', while north of the border it was known as 'the mill'. In these parts, it was simply known as 'the thresher', or 'the machine'. Similarly, the trusser was always referred to as 'the tier', but other parts will have had other names. One of our customers, for example, who had recently moved down from Northumberland, called it 'the bottler'. By the same token, the trusses that it made were referred to in this area as 'battens'. The un-threshed grain was stored in 'stacks', never 'ricks', and also the threshed straw, whether battens or bales, was always 'stacked'.

I have included a section on my early life, a life completely devoid of all modern conveniences. In Chapter 2 – Threshing Tractors and Machinery I have given an account of the tractors, threshers and balers used in our business from 1941 till 1970, and have also listed the tractors and machinery used by other contractors in our vicinity. I have looked at the harvest with binders, stooking the crop and then the carting and stacking. I have written my recollections of a typical days threshing, using either baler or tier, which includes the preparation for an eight o'clock start and the business of moving and setting stacks ready for the next day. A chapter on steam days is included; I do not have first-hand experience of this but this account and the associated stories have been passed down by family and friends over the years. I have described the workings of threshing machines, listing the main manufacturers and agents. The business of moving this equipment on the road is covered with some lighter moments as well as more serious occurrences. There is a section on the meals provided by the farmers' wives, and finally, an account of the last day.

Walter on the left and Eddie on the right mixing concrete. Behind them is machine no. 34769 which always worked with a baler. A wind guard was fitted to the front of the straw walker housing. A row of bales is laid along the top under the sheet.

Chapter 1
Early Life

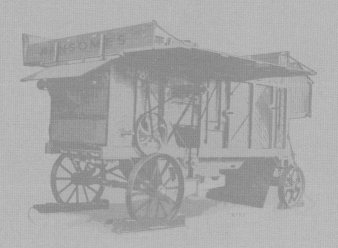

My parents were married in 1942. Grandfather Crisp owned an off farm (a second farm, additional to the main farm) with a big rambling farmhouse. This house was divided into two parts with a large family in one end and we occupied the other. The father of this family and their two eldest sons worked for Grandfather. We had the use of two buildings; one was a workshop and the other housed the fuel tanks and a bench for baling wire and other sundry spares and tools. Part of the yard was used for the parking of machinery.

Some would have described our lifestyle there as somewhat Dickensian, with no mains water, electricity or telephone. This was by no means confined to ourselves. Indeed, at that time, most farms and rural houses in this area had similar lack of amenities.

We had two sources of water; a well situated about 100 yards away from the house, or a rainwater tank at the back of the house. This well was quite a shallow affair, set into a bank side with wood doors on the front. It was built of brick in a square shape, and water ran into it continually, and even in the driest years, it was never known to fail. It was not unknown when going to the well with two enamel buckets for water to find a frog swimming around in it. The frog was usually guided out of the well, with apparently no harmful effects to the contents. A small stream ran past the front of it and took the surplus water that ran out through these doors. The problem occurred when it rained, as this stream took the run-off water from the roofs and yards, which was usually

dirty water and could find its way into the well. So whenever a heavy shower started, people from both families had to get to the well with buckets to ensure a supply of clean drinking water. The well soon cleared as sediment settled in the bottom and cloudy water was washed out under the doors.

The water from the well was good drinking water but the minerals in it that ran from out of the land made it unsuitable for washing as it was virtually impossible to get lather from the soap. It was known as 'hard' water. 'Soft' water, more suitable for washing, came from a storage tank at the back of the house, which collected water off the roof. We were brought up to believe that rainwater was unsuitable for drinking because of the bird droppings on the roof; I am not sure how harmful it really was.

As a result of these primitive arrangements there were no taps in the house, no sinks or wash-basins, no bathroom and, of course, no flush lavatories. Our toiletry needs were taken care of by an 'earth closet' across the yard, which we shared with the other family. This system was common at that time, slowly being replaced as mains water arrived in the 1950s. Even Worsall School, which I attended up to 1956, had earth closets across the yard: two Council refuse collectors climbed into the ash pit behind the toilets and shovelled the area under these closets into an old bath tin and took it to their lorry. Washing-up was done in a large enamel dish on the table, having first boiled a pan or kettle of water. Washing was accomplished in similar fashion. As children, we had a galvanised bathtub in front of the fire but the adults had to make do with an all-over wash.

Because this house had been divided, the other half had what would have been the kitchens with the cooking ranges; we only had a large downstairs room with fireplace and a passage-cum-hallway, which was used as a small kitchen. We had a cooker-cum-stove, made by Valor, which used kerosene. It had two places for pans, and an oven. The coal fire in the room was always lit and the kettle, and very often a pan, would simply be placed on the fire. We had a toasting fork and could make good toast over this fire. Mother had a box iron, which is essentially just that – a box, into which hot inserts of iron would be placed. These inserts, which had a hole near one end, were simply thrown into the fire to be fished out later with

the poker and put into this iron. Washing of clothes was done in a poss tub. This was a round, galvanised tub with ribbed sides and would probably have held twenty gallons of water if full. It would be half-filled and the clothes placed in it with some soap powder, and then the work began. The posser had a shaft similar to a sweeping brush and on the end was a circular copper bell, about one foot in diameter. This was vigorously pushed up and down into the tub for as long as it took to get the clothes clean. We then had a wringer, which fastened to the edge of the table and the tub was placed under it. The wringer consisted of two rollers, turned by a handle on one end, through which the clothes were wound, and the water that was squeezed out could run back into the tub.

We had a Tilley table lamp that provided light in the main room, and we had another oil lamp – a low pressure system using a wick – and an endless supply of candles. Additional heating was provided by a Tilley radiator, which worked on the same principle as the lamp, but a different style of mantle and a copper reflector behind it threw out quite appreciable amounts of heat.

The only form of light entertainment was provided by a valve wireless set. This was powered by batteries that were a world away from the small batteries used in modern transistor radios. Firstly, there was a high tension battery, which

was a dry battery measuring nine inches square by three inches deep – an absolute monster that had a life of approximately six months. In addition there were rechargeable accumulators. These were very similar to a car battery, with glass sides where one could see the lead plates covered with acid. These needed recharging every week, and without mains electricity, they had to be taken to an electrical shop in the nearby town to be recharged. So as part of the weekly shop a used accumulator was taken and exchanged for a fully-charged one.

In 1946, WO had bought a half-acre plot of land on which to build a bungalow and sheds for machinery storage. Restrictions were quite severe in that immediate post-war period. Building licenses were needed and because of the general shortage of materials, the bungalow was restricted in size to 1,000 square feet. There was a water main running past the site, so the bungalow was built with bathroom, sink unit and a further water closet type toilet. It was also fully wired, although mains electricity did not come to the area until 1958.

Eventually it was ready for occupation and the move, which had to be planned not to interfere with a day's threshing, took place on Good Friday, 1951. The kitchen was equipped with an Aga cooker, which was fuelled by coke. It did all the cooking with special Aga

Our only road vehicle from 1946 to 1951 was this Fordson truck. Reg No CVN 886 a powerful vehicle with a V8 petrol engine. Mother took it shopping, it carried fuel and could tow a thresher.

pans and kettle. We had a toaster that consisted of hinged wire grids between which two slices of bread were placed before being put on the hotplate and the lid closed upon it. Aga irons were a big advancement – two base plates that were placed on the hotplate and used alternatively, with one handle piece that fastened to the bases with a twist catch. The Aga also heated the hot water, and it kept the kitchen warm.

Initially we still used the trusted Tilley lamp even though there were light switches and lamp pendants in every room. We had a Petter 3 horsepower petrol/TVO engine that was belted to an overhead shaft, off which was driven a drilling machine, a compressor or a grindstone. In late 1951, WO bought a 110 volt generator, which was mounted on the floor beside this engine and driven by a short belt. From this 110 volt system we had lights in the house but no power. About four lights were ideal; more than that and they became noticeably dimmer. The engine had to be started and stopped by hand, and as I grew older it became my job after school to fill the tank with TVO and start the engine. It would run about six hours on a tank of fuel, so in winter it would simply be left to stop itself when the fuel ran out.

From 1946, our vehicle was a Fordson truck. This was bought as government surplus. It had a truck cab and a wood body, in which two 45 gallon barrels for fuel were secured. The cab was very basic with two seats and the battery was positioned between the seats. A board was laid on the battery, and this was my seat. It was painted a dull shade of red, with cream wheels and mudguards. It was a powerful vehicle with a V8 petrol engine, and in January 1947, WO travelled the 120 miles to Gainsborough with it and towed the new Marshall thresher home. It was sold in 1951 and on the 18th July that year, we took delivery of a new Ford 10 CWT van.

On the 6th September 1951, the Post Office installed our telephone – number Great Smeaton 289. Our lifestyle had advanced more in one year than what it would normally have done in fifty.

In 1956, by some stroke of good fortune, I passed the 11+ examination and then had five years at Yarm Grammar School. This began on the 10th September. It was an exceptionally wet harvest and the Massey Harris combine was having difficulty travelling. A drawbar was fitted to the back of the combine and a tractor with front hitch pushed from behind, with the thresher pushpole. I spent the 9th September driving the tractor doing the pushing. Its registration number was MAJ 384, and the combine's number was MAJ 383.

In March 1958, we were connected to the mains electricity. Two hundred and forty volts gave a brighter light and we were able to have electrical appliances both in the house and in the workshop. The first appliance bought for the house was a mains-powered radio; we had clearly had enough of those accumulators.

Chapter 2

Threshing Tractors and Machinery

WO left school in 1933 to work at home on his father's farm. It was a 120 acre mixed farm with some dairy cows, beef cattle, pigs, hens and, from time to time, sheep. They made hay and grew cereal crops as well as having a small acreage of potatoes and turnips. The field work was all done by one pair of horses, Captain and Charlie, and mechanisation had not been thought of.

His first job after leaving school was carting muck (farmyard manure) into the newly formed potato rows. This involved loading a cart by hand and travelling to the field. The horse was then directed down the rows whilst the muck was pulled out of the cart and placed along the row bottoms. After the whole field – probably four or five acres – had had this treatment the next operation was to walk along the muck placing potato sets at precise spacings along the rows. Finally, Grandfather would split the rows with one horse and rowing plough.

As the spring progressed the next laborious job was 'looking thistles'. In the 1930s, selective weed-killers were not readily available and the practice was to systematically walk over the cereal crops hoeing out all the young thistles. Special hoes were used, which they called 'lookers'. These were essentially a Dutch hoe with a very narrow blade, about two inches wide, so the thistle could be dealt with without damaging the young cereal plants.

As the summer progressed there were the potatoes and turnips to hoe, then the hay and corn harvests were all to be gathered – all with pitchforks and those two trusted horses. The geography of that farm was a long narrow strip of land with the farmyard right in one corner of it. Grandfather liked as much of the produce as possible stored in the stack yard, which meant everything had to be loaded onto carts and transported home to the yard.

WO referred to their neighbours, who were using paddy sweeps with their horses and stacking in the field, and how much quicker that was, but he could not persuade his father to adopt any labour-saving ways. It is little wonder then that WO (who had a good mechanical mind) was to turn away from farming to a more mechanically inclined way of life.

In 1935, they had bought a second-hand International W12 tractor and two-furrow plough. This speeded their operations up considerably and WO was able to do some ploughing for neighbours. This was the start of agricultural contracting that is still going on today.

The 1937 International 10/20 Registration No APY 81 with road bands fitted over its spade lug wheels.

Very few farmers had tractors at this time. Everybody was struggling to get over the Depression years and consequently, there was big demand for his ploughing service. So much so that for the autumn of 1937, they took delivery of a new International 10/20 tractor and bought an additional beam and third furrow for the plough. The tractor was displayed on a stand at Stokesley Show in September of that year, and it was the first International tractor they had seen painted red. Hitherto, they had all been battleship grey.

The contracting business continued to expand, with a set of discs being added. A grass mower and binder were also in service by 1941, when a second-hand Ransomes thresher was bought. This machine was fitted with a Ruston and Hornsby double-band tier and was to give reliable service for several years.

In 1942, WO went on his own with the contracting business, leaving his younger brother to work with the old man and of course, they kept that original 10/20 on the farm. WO bought a second-hand 10/20, and 1942 was also the year that he took delivery of a new International WD6. That WD6 was one of only twenty that came into the country in 1942, and no further diesels came from America for the duration of the war.

The engine in the WD6 was indirect injection, which started on petrol.

The International WD6 Reg No BVN 703 with WO ploughing some rough land circa 1943.
Same tractor same driver 40 years later.

By operating a lever on the driving position the engine was decompressed to allow hand-starting on petrol. After a few minutes running on petrol, the decompression lever and the throttle, which are side by side in the driving position, are drawn upwards and the tractor is switched to diesel fuel. This was a very advanced tractor for its day and it is still in the family today. It was a good threshing tractor; if it had a fault it was the big difference in speed between 4th and 5th gears, with a lot of road work having to be done in 4th gear. As balers were starting to appear, WO felt a bit more power would be useful. He had heard that the WD6's big brother, the WD9, was soon to be available in the UK. He placed an order for one but, unfortunately, no WD9s came to this country under the Lease-Lend scheme (an agreement whereby the then neutral US would send tractors and other machinery to countries at

war with Nazi Germany and Japan but would not expect immediate payment).

In the year that followed, he was offered several other makes of Lease-Lend tractors as they came available, including John Deere A and MMU, but he refused them all until, in late 1943, with an additional thresher on order, he was offered and accepted a Farmall H. The Farmall arrived at Yarm Station in a box, which was how they were shipped from America. The axles and wheels were removed, as was the steering column, exhaust and so on. Everything was secured within this box except the back wheels, which were strapped to the top of it. This packing case was non-returnable and the sides were put to all manner of uses such as spare-part shelves, and one was set up as a bench for the storage of baling wire. The intention was to thresh with the WD6 and the 10/20 and use the Farmall

The Farmall H Reg No CPY 393 in the hay field. The front axle could be adjusted fore and aft. On this occasion in the most forward position to give room for mid mounted row crop equipment, the brackets of which can be seen.

for ploughing and other land work. But things don't always go to plan and over the next few years, the Farmall would do a lot of threshing.

In January 1944, WO took delivery of a new steel-framed Marshall thresher, with a Massey Harris double-band tier. This was wartime, a time of shortages and long waiting lists, and this machine, 34613, had been ordered on pneumatic tyres and a Ruston and Hornsby tier. Apart from the wrong tier it also came to the dealer's yard on steel wheels. Before he took delivery of it they fitted some second-hand lorry axles and wheels but he did, however, initially take the Massey Harris tier.

Nobody liked that Massey Harris tier; it had bad knotters and it did not make very tidy battens. He complained to the dealer and requested in the strongest possible terms that a Hornsby tier be found, to which the dealer replied, "There is a new machine here in the yard with a Hornsby tier on it, and as yet it has nobody's name on it. If you want to bring your machine into the yard and swap tiers over you can do." So that is exactly what they did, and that new machine, number 34769, which will appear later in the story, was now fitted with a Massey Harris tier.

In the war years many things were rationed or in short supply, and one of

All-Steel Frame Thrashing Machines
CLASS "S.M."

The DENNING baler towards the end of its ten year life with us.

the commodities rationed to farmers was binder twine. They were allowed sufficient to binder their crops, but were only allowed enough for one day's threshing. This was for battened straw for thatching, which was considered an essential use for preventing waste on stacks. The remainder of their straw had to be either handled loose or baled, and it was this ruling that created a surge among contractors to buy balers. In 1943, WO had ordered a new Denning baler but no promises were made regarding delivery.
A local engineering firm approached him and said that they were considering making a baler, if he would help with the construction of it. This was agreed and WO spent a good part of the summer of 1943 helping to construct this baler. The design and construction

of this baler would require a chapter on its own, which is beyond the scope of this book. It was, however, not a great success, and so when the new Denning appeared in 1944, that first baler was sold.

The WD6 and the 10/20 were well capable of driving a thresher and baler combined, whilst the Farmall could manage to thresh. They did, however, do one day's threshing and baling only with the Farmall. A farmer in the neighbouring parish had heard them, and said, "We knew what you were doing, even though we could not here the thresher at all. We could hear the retainers on the baler clapping shut and the only other thing we could here was the Farmall screaming."

The 1938 Marshall Model M Reg No JM 4099 which originated in the now defuct country of Westmorland. The heavy duty winch sprag at 45 degrees and heavy ballasted front wheels.

In 1947, WO exchanged the 10/20 for a second-hand Marshall model M fitted with a heavy-duty winch. This was a 1938 model, probably as old as the 10/20 but nevertheless, it did sterling service threshing for the next six years. Being an early Model M it was on 24-inch rear wheels and did not have the high top gear, giving it a road speed of 4½ miles per hour. The round was fairly compact and with a bit of planning, most moves could be kept to less than 5 miles. Most of the time it drove a thresher with Hornsby tier fitted but if needed, it was capable of driving thresher and baler together. Most of the time WO drove the Model M himself. In those days, antifreeze was not generally available, and so in frosty weather, the radiator water had to be drained each evening and filled up again next morning. After a full day's threshing, with the engine completely warm, he used to stand a row of battens of straw around the tractor before sheeting up for the night, and there was sufficient warmth there to keep it safe from frost for one night, without draining the water.

In 1946, there was a second-hand Clayton and Shuttleworth machine on the books, but there is no evidence of it having done much work and it was sold by the end of that year. The Ransomes machine was also sold around this time, clearing the way for another new steel-framed Marshall in January 1947. This

The Field Marshall new January 1948 Reg EAJ 752. Threshing at Carr House, Great Smeaton, the belt can just be seen passing the end bay of sheaves in the Dutch Barn. This picture was taken in this tractors first year, the series two cap can be seen on the air intake. This was replaced with a "Burgess" oil bath cleaner early in 1949.

new machine was fitted with proprietary pneumatic tyres and brakes on the rear axle. It was fitted with a self-feeder and Marshall 'chaff and cavings' blowers, and a portable Ruston and Hornsby tier was included in the package. The advantage to the portable tier was that when baling, the tier was pulled clear, allowing the straw to fall directly into the baler. This tier, however, wasn't popular. They seemed to have difficulty keeping it stationary, it moved around till the driving chain jumped off the sprockets and it didn't make a very tidy batten, so after one year it was sold and a mounted one fitted. The self-feeder and the chaff blowers were not proving popular, so they were removed and sold at this time.

In 1948, WO sold the WD6 and the Farmall to his father and brother, who by now were on a larger farm, and he took delivery of a new Series Two Field Marshall. This was a reliable and economical threshing tractor fitted with a built-in heavy-duty winch, its big advantage over the WD6 being its exceptional traction. So from 1948 onwards, there were two Marshall tractors and two Marshall threshers, both fitted with mounted Hornsby double-band tiers. It would be fair to say that neither Marshall did much work other than belt and winch work, but with a hundred days threshing each, haystacks were baled and hay was baled in the field, and together with wood sawing and such like, they were kept fairly busy.

In 1948, WO also bought a second-hand Standard Fordson. This was an ex 'War-Ag' tractor. The War Agricultural Executive Committee had been set up in 1939 by the Ministry of Agriculture to help farmers increase the output from their land. In this area it was the North Riding War Agricultural Executive Committee (NRWAEC, shortened to War-Ag). WO's tractor was a 1943 model with narrow mudguards and fitted with a belt pulley and power take-off. This was not bought as a threshing tractor but it was pressed into service occasionally as it was capable of driving a thresher. In fact, its belt pulley horsepower would be the same as the E27N Major, and on one day in 1948, it did one day's threshing and baling. The problem with a Standard Fordson on belt work was that it hadn't an independent handbrake, so it was necessary to chock the wheels to keep the belt tight.

In 1951, he bought a second-hand E27N Fordson Major, with high top gear, which was less than two years old. Again, it was intended primarily as a land work tractor, being equipped with hydraulic lift, as well as PTO and belt pulley, and at this time it was our fastest road tractor. It came in for increasing amounts of threshing as by 1952, we were running three threshing sets.

In harvest time we also offered a corn-cutting service with the binder. Initially this was a Hornsby ground drive machine, which was exchanged for an Albion power-driven one for use with the Farmall. From 1948 onwards, a power-driven Sunshine of 6-foot cut was used with the Standard Fordson. In the early 1950s we were running two binders, the Sunshine with the Fordson, and an 8-foot cut McCormick power-driven one with the Fordson Major. The custom was that only one man went with the binder, with the farmer left to provide a man to ride on it. This was very often a job that the farmer undertook himself. If there was a problem or small hold-up in proceedings the farmer would stand and watch as the problem was rectified, lending a hand if required. But one farmer, who had little mechanical instinct, would not do this. Instead he would set a stook up while he waited. On completing the field and looking over it, there were these occasional stooks dotted across the field as a memorial to every stop that there had been. By the mid 1950s, work was declining and both binders were replaced by a 6-foot Bisset, which was used on Fordson Major Diesels into the mid 1960s.

In 1952, when the older thresher was involved in an accident (which is dealt with in a later chapter), keeping it out of work for most of that year, a replacement was sought. After several futile attempts a suitable machine was

Taken on 23rd June 1953 the day this tractor was new. Supplied by John Neasham of Darlington for £639. The first Fordson Major diesel we had seen with a vertical exhaust. The badge on the front grill commemorates the Queens Coronation.

located at a nearby contractor's yard. It happened to be 34769, which we last left fitted with a Massey Harris tier. By now, the tier was no longer with it, although the mounting frames were still on. As by this time much more straw was being baled, this machine was not fitted with a tier again but worked all the time in conjunction with a baler.

Demand for baling straw and hay increased gradually throughout the 1940s, not only out of the stack in winter but also in the field in summer. In 1952, a new Davies baler was added, and that baler is still in my ownership. In the next two years, two stationary balers were in use, and with pick-up balers still in their infancy, it is easy to forget how

much work these balers did. There were days in those years when only the third threshing set with the Fordson Major was threshing; the other two gangs with the Marshalls would both be baling hay. In summer, the baler would be set in a hayfield and the pikes would be swept to the back of it and forked in. This was indeed full-time work and each baler would be doing upwards of 200 days' work a year.

In 1953, the old Model M was exchanged for a more up-to-date one. This was a 1943 model with 28-inch back wheels and a high top gear. We retained the winch from the old one. By this time, there were two stationery balers and this tractor was doing

The 1955 Fordson Major. On the scrub clearance job in 1956. No hydraulics on this tractor, the Lainchbury winch and Winsam cab can be seen, together with oversize tyres and wheel weights. The driver would eventually go on to write a book on Threshing days.

increasing amounts of threshing and baling. Although it managed to drive them adequately in work, on the road, with that high top gear, it was prone to clutch-slip on any form of uphill slope and consequently, second gear was the only option.

June 1953 saw the end of TVO tractors as both the Fordsons gave way to a new Fordson Major Diesel, complete with a coronation badge on its front grill. This was the first of these tractors we had seen with a vertical exhaust pipe. Intended primarily for land work, it also did many days threshing.

From 1952 till 1954, we ran three threshing sets, although it has to be said that the third one was not in full-time use, but it did give the opportunity for the two newest machines to be sent away to be fitted with chaff blowers and to be re-sprayed.

In 1954 there were two machinery changes. The Denning baler was sold in part exchange for the first pick-up baler, and the oldest thresher was similarly replaced with a second-hand Massey Harris 726 combine. Selling the Denning baler at this time proved to be a misjudgement. Although farmers were ready for pick-up balers for hay there was still more demand for straw in the larger stationary bales than one baler could cope with. Consequently, a second-hand Powell stationary baler was bought and used for two years, from whence more people were prepared to use pick-up balers to bale off the thresher.

From this time onward, WO's thoughts and discussions centred around what was to replace the ageing Marshall tractors. The first criterion was that ideally they should have the belt pulley mounted on the left-hand side of the

Dinner time. Threshing at Village Farm Dalton on Tees. The Boughton winch can be clearly seen on the Nuffield 460 on this occasion without cab. A rather tidy straw stack is visible.

tractor. The two that complied with this were the Nuffield and the David Brown 50D. The Nuffield at this time had the sliding rear hubs with the half-shafts protruding some 8 inches beyond the tyre, and it was felt that this would create problems in confined stack yards, where the tractor sometimes had to be tight up to buildings or gate posts. The David Brown also had sliding hubs but the half-shafts were not as long as those on the Nuffield. The David Brown was favourite, and WO had lengthy discussions with a representative of our local dealership, but nothing came of it. I suspect the reason was probably the price; Fordsons or Nuffields were around £600, but the David Brown was over £800. This may not seem a convincing reason but it must be remembered that in those days, a day's threshing with two men brought in £8.

In March 1955, the decision was made. The left-hand pulley idea was abandoned, and a new Fordson Major was bought to replace the Model M Marshall. This tractor had no hydraulics, but was fitted with a Lainchbury winch and a Winsam cab. It had 14-30 rear tyres and 7.50-16 fronts. A sturdy front drawbar made it a complete threshing tractor.

The Field Marshall was sold in early 1957, and from then through until 1964, a succession of Fordson Majors were used. They were purposeful and reliable, and the drivers liked them. If they had a fault it was in the gearing of the pulley, which was a two-speed pulley depending on the position of the high/low gear lever. In the high ratio with a standard 9-inch diameter pulley on the drum shaft, at the required drum speed the tractor engine ran at 1,200rpm. This was really too slow; with pneumatic governors it was liable to lose speed when threshing and baling fast. At one time, one of the machines had an 11-inch drum pulley and this allowed the tractor to run at 1,400rpm, which was a big improvement. One contractor we knew had a 9-inch pulley fitted to his tractor, an 8-inch one on the drum shaft, and threshed in low ratio.

By the late 1950s, threshing was noticeably reducing and when in 1960, safety guards became compulsory, WO declared that he would guard one machine, but one only. So in the spring of 1960, 34769 was sold through a collective machinery sale, making £54. From then on we only had 35562, which is still in my ownership.

By 1962, we had bought a new Nuffield 460 for land work. It didn't have a belt pulley, but in winter months drove a pick-up baler, baling straw off the thresher. Threshing was now very much in decline, but we had an active land drainage business that had use for a better winch, and so in 1964, that Nuffield was taken as a threshing tractor. It was fitted with a pulley, Winsam cab and a Boughton two-speed winch. It was a good threshing tractor with a noticeable increase in power over the Fordsons but it had independent PTO. When using a winch, whether it be pulling trees or a pipe-laying mole drainer, you sometimes need to stop instantly, and one's natural reaction in those circumstances is to depress the clutch pedal. For those of us used to that hand clutch it wasn't too much of a problem, but we sometimes had people driving it who were not as familiar with the Nuffield, and we felt there was a potential danger.

What we needed was a standard drive Nuffield 460. Well, as it happened, we had one. It also was a 1962 model fitted with a Shawnee Warrior excavator/loader combination that was now getting hard-worn. We were able to sell the Shawnee equipment from it and retain the tractor. It had been painted yellow so it was re-sprayed and the cab and winch were transferred from the other Nuffield. This one had the benefit of 14-30 rear and 7.50-18 front tyres. It was an ideal set up – probably our best threshing tractor, and certainly our last.

In 1966 I accepted a job baling straw off somebody else's thresher. It was a Foster machine driven by a series III Field Marshall, but it only had one drum pulley. I used the 460 to drive the baler from the front end, and this meant standing between the belt and the baler to needle-and-tie the wires. This was something that had been done regularly in the past when baling hay out of the field, but it was the first time I had done it. There wasn't much room in there. The baler front axle was turned into the square lock so that the front wheel was no longer in the way, and when needling, your arm had to go out between the top and bottom of the belt to press the needle down on the bottom section of the belt to align it with the slots in the bale chamber when inserting the needle. There were two days of this – on a Monday and a Tuesday. There were all kinds of work pressures at that time and so we found ourselves with a half-day threshing for our own machine booked in for the Tuesday afternoon. It was with the farmer's own pick-up baler. George, my part-time feeder man, could manage to thresh on his own: the problem was a tractor. Most of our tractors were fully occupied with other work and the only one we had available was a Nuffield Universal Three, which we used for the lighter field work. I moved the machine into this farm and set it to the stack on the Saturday before with the 460. We had a spare Nuffield pulley and so that was fitted, George went off and did his

The Nuffiled Universal Three did half a days threshing. It did a lot of work with a Cameron Gardner Rearloader hence the front weight. A 1960 model registration no 583 GUP.

half-day's threshing with the Nuffield Three, and it has always been a regret of mine that I was not there to witness it.

I should just a briefly mention the machinery used by our 'competitors'. The three main makes of English thresher would be used in equal numbers. Ransomes were probably the most numerous, with Fosters and Marshalls being well represented. Wood-framed Marshalls were in use right up until the 1960s. There were also several Clayton machines in use and in the post-war years, some of

One of Charles Turner & Sons Ltd Fordson Majors. This is a T V model wit Lainchbury winch and traction engine style roof. John Neashman of Darlington supplied six of these tractions with cast raer wheels. They took a 13 X 28 inch tyre and were aimed at the threshing or similar uses. It is now fully restored by the present owner David Robinson.

the Scottish makes appeared – mainly Garvie and Crichton. One day, I was in conversation with an old thresher man beside a Crichton. He had spent a lifetime with Marshall and Foster machines and he said of this Crichton, "No self-respecting thresher man would be seen with one of these things." What he was referring to was the fact that the belt pulleys were flat and not 'crowned', as was the case with English machines, which helped to keep flat belts gripping and on the pulleys.

There was a wide range of balers in use. The most numerous were probably Jones, but Powell, Ransomes, Denning and Davies were also to be seen regularly. Turner's of Lazonby used Bonell balers, their notable feature being their extremely long bale chamber, which held an additional bale compared to other makes. The baler that appeared to gain in popularity, particularly in the 1950s, was the Reffold.

Traction engines were replaced by tractors in the 1940s; Marshalls were prominent as the main British manufacturers of tractors suitable for the job, although Fordsons were used in increasing numbers. The American imports under the Lease-Lend scheme would also play a significant role as threshing tractors. Most of these were suitable. The Internationals, I have mentioned, but Case, Oliver and MM were also widely used. In the late 1940s,

the E27N Major fitted with a Perkins Diesel engine was favoured by many. The road haulage firm Preston's of Potto were threshing contractors from 1936 until 1957. At their sale there were five threshing sets: two Fosters, one wood-framed Marshall, one steel-framed Marshall and a Clayton. There were four balers: two Jones and two Reffolds. And tractors: two Fordson Majors fitted with Perkins P6 engines, one Series Two Field Marshall, an Oliver 90 and an MM UDS with Meadows engine. I would say that this was a fair representation of equipment used at that time.

Charles Turner and Sons were from Lazenby, a small village on the southern edge of industrial Teesside, in the vicinity of Redcar. Their threshing sale was in July 1959, with six threshers – three Fosters, two Marshalls and one Ransomes – all fitted with Hornsby double-band tiers. There were also four balers – two Bonells and two Jones Tigers, and seven tractors – two David Brown Thresherman tractors, four Fordson Majors (two with Perkins P6 engines and two TVO types), and one Series Two Field Marshall. There was also a Fowler Compound Traction Engine, which sold for £260.

Threshing work was also carried out by the War Agricultural Committee both during and after the Second World War. They set up local depots to provide a contracting service to carry out all types of farm work wherever there was a need and they became involved in a lot of work in the marginal areas. The War-Ag was tasked with enforcing legislation that required farmers to plough out a fixed percentage of their grassland to grow cereal crops on, and many small farms that had been all grass for many years had to plough grassland out to grow arable crops. This meant that farms well up in the Yorkshire Dales and on the North Yorks Moors were now growing cereals.

In the 1960s, we had an ex-War-Ag man employed driving a Track Marshall. He could recount stories of threshing high up in the Dales, where access was by long, sometimes steep, rutted roads, making it very difficult to negotiate with tractor and thresher, so in the worst areas they used a Caterpillar D2 to pull the machine to the farms and then drive the thresher with a rear-mounted belt pulley. I recently looked at a steel Marshall machine with the letters N R W A E C written on the side of the straw walker housing. This was a late machine, probably 1950, but the War-Ag were still able to buy a new thresher as late as that. Our Track Marshall driver was able to say that in 1954, all North Riding War-Ag depots were supplied with a new tractor. This was a Fordson Major Diesel to ministry specifications: no lights, no belt pulley and no handbrake. Their Smallways depot, which is close to the Dales, wanted a tractor for threshing, so they were supplied with two – one with the same specification

as other depots and one with full specification for use as a threshing tractor.

To the west of us a man by the name of Ingram Miller threshed and did other contract work. He had a heavy Ransomes machine, Jones baler and an MM UDS with a Dorman engine. Later, he used a Fordson Power Major. He once ploughed a field for a customer and on completion he asked how big the field was, to which the chap replied, "It's called six acres but there is a pylon, a haystack and a muck midden in it so there will be a bit to knock off." Ingram replied, "There's nowt to knock off. I would rather have ploughed them bits as ploughed round 'em."

Local contractor Ted Kirby was a Fordson man, using a heavy Ransomes machine and Powell stationary baler, and later, Jones pick-up balers. His tractors were first an E27N fitted with a Perkins L4 engine, and then two E1A Majors – a Power Major and Super Major. In his last few years he used a Ford 4000 with a rear-mounted belt pulley.

Everybody involved at that time would have had their own preferences, much as is the case today. For those who are connoisseurs of the exhaust note of vintage tractors, if the opportunity ever arises I would draw to your attention that of an Oliver 80 driving a thresher.

A front view of MAJ 384. Pulling our Welger AP15 baler. The front hitch can be clearly seen. It was necessary to remove one headlamp to allow the driving belt clearance when threshing with a Fordson Major. The March 1955 tracrtor still had the narrow exhaust pipe.

Preston's sale day, July 1957.

Chapter 3

The Harvest

Maternal Grandfather, William Crisp.
3 Horses pulling a binder in the 1930's.

The grain reaper was essentially the same design as a grass mower, with a reciprocating knife running in fingers, very similar to the modern combines. The early reapers required two men, one of whom drove the two horses required to pull it. Behind the cutter bar on a grain reaper was a platform on which the crop fell to be raked off in bunches by the second man, and then be tied up into sheaves by other workers following behind. The next development was the sail reaper, often known as the 'self-raking reaper'. Only one man was required on this as the sails revolved at such a speed that each time one passed over the cutter bar platform, there was the correct amount of material there to form a sheaf, which was then swept off onto the ground.

It was back-breaking work, very often done by women who followed the reapers around the fields tying these sheaves up. They took two small handfuls of the straw and twisted the ends together to form 'bands', which were placed around the sheaf, twisted together again, and the sheaf was completed. In the latter years of the nineteenth century, attempts

Isaac Bainbridge cutting corn in the 1930's. Accompanied by his daughters and friend. The horse whip is visible by his right hand.

were being made around the world to mechanise this tying up of the sheaves. The Americans were working with wire-tying binders, but it was Claas, of Germany, who perfected the twine-tying knotter. By the end of that century, twine-tying binders were being manufactured by many firms in various places around the world.

The binder starts off, as did the reaper, with a reciprocating knife, but above it run the sails, much lighter than those used on the reapers, which direct the crop backwards onto a canvass. This is the platform canvass that transports the crop sideways to the bottom of the elevator canvasses. There are two of these, running in opposite directions, that pass the crop between them and

elevate it up to the tying mechanism. Under the platform of the tier there is a crankshaft, onto which tines known as packers are fitted. These compress the crop against retaining feet at the base of the tier. Another essential component of a binder is the 'butter' – a reciprocating paddle that runs against the base of the crop stems, making them smooth and even. When the density within the forming sheaf has reached a pre-set level, the tying mechanism is tripped; the needle enters from below, bringing twine around the sheaf to the knotter, where it is tied and the twine cut before the needle returns to its rest to await the next sheaf being formed. The knotter mechanism is mounted on the top shaft of the tier. As the tying cycle is activated, gear

John Banks of Fishlocks Farm Low Dinsdale. Taken in 1932 the year that the Ruston and Hornsby binder was new. On the occasion pulled by Dapper, Prince and Farmer.

teeth within the cam wheel engage with two pinions, one of which revolves the 'bill hook', which forms the knot. The second one revolves the twine retainer, which releases the twine on the sheaf that has now been completed, and collects and holds the twine for the sheaf about to be formed. On that top shaft are ejector arms, which also revolve and eject the sheaf. At the same time, the compressor feet retract, allowing the newly formed sheaf a clear exit onto the ground.

Binders took over from reapers around the turn of the twentieth century. This was a major advancement in farm mechanisation, saving the back-breaking work of preparing bands from crop and tying them. When a new binder was delivered to this farm in the early years of the twentieth century, the dealer's men came out to set it off, which was in a field with a ditch running through it, known in this area as a 'stell'. Having seen it go the first time around, Great-Grandfather's comment was that "She tied every one, and winged 'em all down into the stell."

Binders were at this time drawn with horses and as they took quite some effort to pull them, three horses were needed. The majority of binders were left hand-cut, although right-hand cut ones did exist. The man on the binder not only had to control these three horses but also operate the controls of the binder. There were normally four main controls on a binder; one

By 1946 John Banks had passed on and the Binder had been converted for use behind a tractor. The green Fordson on spade lug wheels is being driven by Elsie Banks.

controlled the cutting height, two levers controlled the height and fore and aft movement of the sails, and the fourth lever moved the tier fore and aft. This was an essential control to ensure that the band was in the centre of the sheaf, so whether it was long oats or short barley that was being cut, the twine would always be in the centre of the sheaf. This was an extremely skilled job and on medium sized farms it was normally the farmer himself who took responsibility. The normal size of cut on horse-drawn binders was 5 or 6 feet. The drive was taken from a large wheel that ran underneath the tier, and even when tractors took over, 6 feet was considered large enough for ground drive binders. Binders were transported by fitting road wheels back and front and re-positioning the drawbar in the end of the platform, and towing it endways to reduce its width to a more suitable one for narrow lanes and gateways.

Binders on the market in this country were made in several parts of the world. The home produced ones were Albion and Hornsby. Massey Harris were made in Canada, whilst their Australian subsidiary turned out the Sunshine models. McCormick and Deering had amalgamated to form the International Harvester Co in 1902, but nevertheless, both firms produced their own binder – in the case of McCormick, up until the 1950s. John Deere made

The Bisset semi mounted binder in working mode, highlighting the vee belt drives.

The 6 foot cut Bissett binder in transport mode.

binders in the United States, some of which were imported into the United Kingdom, but they never enjoyed the popularity of McCormick or Massey Harris. On Continental Europe there were numerous makes. Probably the best known to us was the Lanz, and in the post-war years, J F produced an interesting binder with the tier low down on the end of the platform canvass.

As tractors took over from horses to pull binders, so binders driven by the tractor power take-off (PTO) became available. With power-driven binders the width of cut increased in this country up to 8 feet, although some parts of the world went up to ten feet. All these major manufacturers continued to fit a separate seat on the binder with the controls positioned to the occupier of

that seat. Close to the seat was a cast-iron socket designed to carry a whip for the binder man to control the horses, and this socket continued to be fitted on tractor binders. One pair of elderly brothers, when using a tractor with one of them on the tractor and one on the binder, the binder man still carried the whip, and if he wanted to stop he would crack the whip on the tractor mudguard. An interesting design used in the United States was remote control of the tractor from the binder seat, so that the man on the binder also controlled the tractor, making this a one-man operation.

It was a Scottish firm who were to completely redesign the binder. Bisset's, of Blairgowrie, had been makers of conventional binders for many years, but after the Second World War came up with their new design. As by now

The WD6 with McCormick 8 foot cut power driven binder.

all tractors had PTO and hydraulics, the first thing they realised was that the large steel wheel, which had been used to power the ground drive binder, was no longer needed. It was replaced with two small rubber tyre castor wheels behind the machine, the front of which was now carried on the lower hydraulic lift arms of the tractor. For transportation, the sails were removed and the cutting table was lifted into the vertical position, as happened with grass mowers, and brackets on the tier held the sails in place. The seat was not fitted; instead, the levers were now positioned at the front of the machine where the tractor driver could operate them. The other major change was that the chains on the rear of the binder were replaced by V belts. These binders were, however, still left-hand cut.

Nineteen-fifty-six was an extremely wet harvest and ground conditions were very soft. Many binders were still of the ground drive variety, which were quite useless in these conditions. Many farmers bought new binders in that year, most of which were Bissets, but I knew of one farmer who bought a new Albion. By this time under the David Brown influence, it was painted red and carried the name of 'David Brown Albion'.

The normal working method for a binder was round and round, but if crops were laid, you sometimes had to miss the side where the crop was laid away from the binder, and in extreme cases, fields would have to be cut one way. Lifters were available for binders, which were longer than the ones used on combines, because they not only lifted the crop but also kept it straight across the platform canvass. Some farmers used the socket that had been intended to carry the horse whip to carry a fork, which he used to help straighten the crop in difficult conditions. With combines, once the knife is under the crop it doesn't matter much which way the stems are presented to the auger, but on a binder it did matter, as all the straw needed to be in the same direction to enable a uniform and neat sheaf to be made.

There were several different ways of starting into a field, some of the old hands used to like to mow a tractor width round the field, and the mown crop would then need to be hand-tied and the sheaves stood up against the hedge. Some would cut a time round 'the wrong way', with the tractor running out in the crop. The sheaves would be ejected into the standing crop and somebody would have to follow the binder around the field removing these sheaves before a start could be made going the opposite way, and again standing them against the hedge. Others would simply start as normal and leave a cut around the hedge back to be cut later, after the sheaves had been removed from it. This would sometimes be difficult to cut as it had been knocked down by the passing tractor wheels, and it could well have necessitated the fitting of crop lifters. In standing crops the usual pattern of cutting was round and round the field.

On reaching the corner the binder would continue straight until the knife had cut clear of the crop, and then – in the case of a left-hand cut – the horses/tractor would turn sharply left with the end of the cutter bar entering the crop first, and eventually, the full width would be in the crop. This left a pointed corner to the crop, because binders were not easy to reverse, and with sheaves laid all over the field it was not possible to loop round at corners. With Bissets it was possible to reverse on corners, and that became the accepted way of turning.

As the material entered the tier on the binder, the packers that compressed the sheaf did so in such a way that it was tightly compressed in the form of a letter C, with the open part being near the top where the knot was formed. When stooking the sheaves, one picked first one, then a second sheaf and hoisted them up under each arm, with the knots nearest one's body. They were then stood up on the ground in a V formation, with the open side of the sheaf towards the inside of the stook. It was customary to make stooks with ten sheaves in each and taking five binder rows to one stook row. One started up the middle of these five rows and took the first and second sheaf to begin the stook, and then did the same with the other four rows to complete it. All stooks pointed the same way; my grandfather said you position your stook to point to the one o'clock sun. One o'clock was because of British summer

Betty Roy (later Harrison) of the Womens Land Army. Loading sheaves on a four wheel trailer at Breakhouse Farm Eryholme.

time, the intention being to give both sides of the stook the same exposure to the sun.

The time that the crop was left in stook varied, mainly on the weather, but about two weeks would be about normal. One of the old sayings passed down over the years was that 'Stooks should hear the church bells ring thrice.' This probably applied to oats, which could be cut a little on the green side, but if wheat and barley were ripe when cut, less time in the stook would be required. In very wet years it was quite common for the tops of stooks to green over with sprouted grains. Another problem could be getting the bottoms of the sheaves dry. It was common practice to under-sow grass seeds into growing cereal crops.

If the grass seeds established well and grew up into the bottoms of the stooks it was sometimes necessary to go round the day before stacking the crop and pulling the stooks onto their sides to dry the sheaf bottoms.

In drier parts of the world it was quite common to thresh in the field without stacking the crop. The machine would be set in the field and trailer-loads of sheaves would be drawn alongside and forked directly onto the thresher. Threshing 'out of stook', as it was known, was practised to a certain extent in this country, but from the 1950s onwards, if a farmer wanted some grain at harvest time he would combine a field. It was usual for a farmer to thresh some wheat very early in the season;

Stacking in the Dutch Barn at East Worsall Farm. The E27N Major would date this photograph to the late 1940's or early 50's. The end bay is full of hay in wire tied bales from a stationary baler.

Stack yard at Girsby Grange late 1930's. Christopher Alderson driving the horse. His son Tom sitting in the wagon.

the grain would be required for autumn seed and the straw would be needed for thatching or potato clamps. It was noticeable that as the work was decreasing the first thing to go was the early autumn threshing as farmers began to combine what would have been their first day's threshing.

To load sheaves onto a trailer the first step was to lay a row of them down each side of the trailer with their heads into the centre. On average sized trailers a further row down the centre would overlap the two outside rows. This was known as a 'course'. The next step was to lay a row across each end again, with butt ends out over, then go across again overlapping onto the end row, and do this as often as needed depending on the length of trailer. This was known as a 'filling'. The load was always finished with a filling and sometimes two, with the top one being narrower than the first. In most cases the load would travel to the stack without ropes, but on long, uneven farm tracks roping was sometimes necessary.

At the stack yard there were various ways of building a stack. Some people made round stacks. In my experience, this was because the crop was not very dry and would dry better in a small stack, or it may have been that there was deemed to be insufficient material for a larger stack. In 1965, following a wet harvest, quite a bit of wheat was stacked in small round stacks and when

threshing them, it was possible to save moving the machine to move the stack. The winch rope would be passed around the stack, three or four of the men would hold fencing stakes upright around the back of the stack to prevent the rope cutting into it, and it could then be winched up to the side of the machine. A rectangular stack sufficient for half a day's threshing would measure 10 yards by 4 yards. There was, however, this technique known as 'springing' the stack. This was where each course that was laid protruded slightly over the one below. A stack that allegedly started as 10 x 4 could be 12 x 6 at the easing (the point where the topping-out began).

It was essential to have a good thick stack bottom in order to ensure that all the grain was kept dry. Some farmers began by placing thorns on the ground first, which were then covered by straw. Others just used a thick layer of straw. On the assumption that it was a 10 x 4 stack, they went to the centre of the base 2 yards in from the end and placed one sheaf cross-over the stack. Then they placed one sheaf with its head on the first one, pointing longitudinally along the stack, then placed two more with their heads together on this one, and their butts either side of it. They'd carry on the length of the stack placing sheaves in this formation, each one overlapping the previous ones. They then started to go around this formation placing sheaves with their heads on this triple arrangement and their butts pointing to the outside of the stack. They kept on going round and round in this fashion until the required size of stack was reached. Having reached the required size the next step was to start again with a row of sheaves, again with heads pointing to the centre of the stack, half-lapping the outer row and the second one. After that, they'd carry on round and round the stack to the centre, each row half-lapped onto the previous one. This was known as the 'filling'. It was essential to keep the centre of the stack full, or higher than

the outside, so that the stems were inclined down over to the outside, and then water would run out and not enter the stack. There were varying ways of turning the corners. Some made a square-ended stack and simply turned corners by placing sheaves on the corner at right angles to the previous one, while others built round-ended stacks.

There were two ways of stacking practised; some could do it all with a fork whilst others preferred to stack on their knees. My grandfather would stack

Stacking at Girsby Grange late in the 1920's. Christopher Alderson is stacking, one of his elder daughters is picking in a long dress. His son Charlie is forking the load
The wagon was on this farm till 1980 when it was donated to a local mueseum.

the middle with a fork but would then stick the fork in the stack and get down on his knees to go around the outside. The time around the outside was known as a 'course', and the centre was the filling. Whichever way was adopted, the practice was to lay the sheaf slightly overlapping the previous one, and then continue, either standing or kneeling on it. This process was only too apparent on threshing days, where the man forking had to go around the stack in the opposite direction to which it had been built. When the stack was low the man forking off the trailer could place them close enough to the stacker for him to reach, but this was not possible when the stack got higher. An additional person was needed on the stack to fork sheaves from where the trailer man pitched them to close proximity to the stacker. This was known as 'picking on the stack'. I have done many days of it.

'Topping out the stack' was a slightly different technique. Having reached the required height the procedure was to stack one or two additional filler courses to keep the stack's centre even higher. Then go round the outside with

Grandfather Crisp stacking on his knees, the forker is Peter Watson.

Dated August 1961. Farmer George Stainthorpe driving the tractor, his assistant on the load is Johnny Clough.

sheaves at forty-five degrees, followed by another filling, with sheaves laid onto the heads of the outer course to hold them in place. This was repeated, with the stack becoming narrower all the time until a point was reached. There were various ways of finishing the top. Very often, some straw was placed along the ridge. If the intention was to thatch the stack it would just be left until such time as that could be done.

Thatching of corn stacks was something of an option. A good stacker could make a stack top that no water could penetrate. I encountered a problem when threshing un-thatched stacks when there was a deep covering of snow. Although the forkers went round each course trying to knock snow off the outer sheaves before forking onto the machine, snow did get into the machine, which caused problems – particularly with the baler, where it was a constant job adjusting the bale tension.

Thatching, again, was a highly skilled job, done mostly off a ladder. A batten of straw would be taken up the ladder to where the topping had begun, and this was spread out to the right of the ladder (or left, in the case of a left-handed man), keeping the straw straight and vertical. The traditional way of holding in place was to have a series of hazel sticks, about 2 feet long, and push one into the stack at arm's length, and then another close to the ladder. The outer ends would be connected with

Stacking with an elevatror in the 1950's at Girsby Grange. Charlie is the stacker, his sister Millie is the picker. Nora Capps is the tractor driver. Tom and nephew Alf on the trailer with Roy the dog.

binder twine, and the sticks pushed in a little further till the twine became tight over the thatch. In this part of the world they were known as 'stack stobs' but in the latter years, they were very rarely used. Instead, the whole stack would be covered by a net.

Having got the first batten in position, a second would be carried up and spread out above the first with a suitable overlap. The thatcher would then carry on until the ridge was reached, when it would be time to move the ladder about a yard to the left and start the process over again. This would be repeated until the whole stack was covered. Some would not claim to have finished harvest until all the stacks were thatched. The expression I have heard was 'We are all thatched-up.'

In the early years of the twentieth century, with more labour on farms, some men went to great lengths to make stacks as attractive as possible. The base of the thatch would be trimmed round with shears to give it a nice neat line, and the ridge would similarly be trimmed, and in some cases, some ornamentation made out of straw would be added.

Dick Lovelace standing in front of his recently completed corn stack.

Les Walker prepares for a vintage working day. Two magnificent loads of sheaves close to perfection.

Chapter 4

Threshing Day

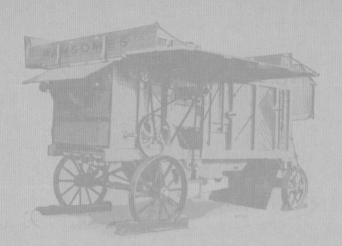

The stack yard at the Ashes, Low Dinsdale in 1943. A confined space for a traction engine to maneuver a threshing machine.

In the years that I was threshing, from 1964 to 1970, it was very much a part-time activity. Consequently, I had a part-time feeder man. He had a small farm with twenty cows, so the earliest time he could start work was eight o'clock. So for those years I had to open the machine out and get everything ready for eight o'clock on my own.

This is where reality differs from what happens at today's working demonstrations, where it is warm, bright daylight with no time pressures. The following is my description of getting the machine ready to thresh and bale using a stationary baler, or a Ruston and Hornsby trusser.

I nearly always travelled to work on the tractor, which had been fuelled the night before, and I needed to be there by 7.15 am. In winter months it was dark when I arrived, very often frosty, but always cold. One would be struck by the silhouette of these enormous corn stacks that seemed to dwarf the thresher standing between them. The first job was to go round loosening the sheet ropes, which on frosty mornings

were stiff and cold. I tried working with gloves on, but some knots were difficult to undo so the gloves had to come off.

Next, the scaffolding boards were pushed up and the stay rods fitted into the frame member. The ladder, which was carried behind the shaker belt resting on the shaker shaft ends, could then be accessed. It was then time to get up on top and fold the sheet up. This was much easier with two men – one at the front, the other at the rear – to pull the sides of the sheet in to form a neat row along the centre of the machine. It was not as easy with one man, but obviously it could be done. The first step was to fold in the end flaps; one covered the tier and the other the back blast, and hung down the back. When this had been done and the sides folded in, it was then a case of starting at the back and rolling it up to the front of the machine. The exception to this was in strong winds, when the sheet was simply pulled off onto the ground, folded on the ground and then carried up the ladder back onto the top of the machine.

Our threshers were always covered with straw on top to hold the sheet in a rounded form to allow water to run off more freely. On a machine that never worked with a baler this was done with battens, which were thrown down each morning and replaced by new ones at the end of the day. Others carried a row of bales down the centre, which were

kept on top and used many times over. It would be starting to get light as the vertical boards were fitted and secured and the drum lid opened up. Then the tier was to be wound down and the straw board (for taking the straw across to the baler) was stood in the tier to be secured later. We carried the driving belts on top of the machine and the last job on top was to throw these down. Then it was a quick look at the watch; if I was at that stage by twenty to eight, I should have plenty of time.

On the ground it was a matter of setting the baler. It had usually been left in front of the machine approximately in the correct line, but now, with daylight, you were able to check this and correct it if necessary. We normally used the front drawbar on the tractor to push the baler back, as it was easier to correct any misalignment. The belt was now placed on the pulleys and tightened by drawing the baler forward. The Davies baler had some good iron chocks and supports; on stoned roads or yards these were excellent as the baler never moved with these in place. On soft ground, I didn't always use them but relied on digging holes in the ground in precisely the right place so that the baler just rolled into the holes to tighten the belt. The advantage to this was that it gave a little more slope on the straw board, which was laid over the tier.

The straw board was now secured in place, and the tractor taken to the

The steel Marshall thresher and Davies baler. The wheel chocks supplied with the baler are in position.

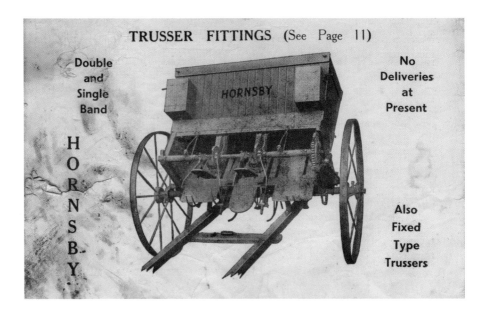

TRUSSER FITTINGS (See Page 11)

Double and Single Band

No Deliveries at Present

HORNSBY

HORNSBY

Also Fixed Type Trussers

An extract from the United Manufacturing Company March 1945 catalogue

back of the machine and lined up and the belt fitted. By this time, the farm staff would be there with sacks and whatever else was needed at the corn end – sometimes a weighing machine, sometimes a sack lift, but generally a door or something of that nature to be placed under the sacks on the machine. The job that I left till last was setting out and securing the chaff pipes because by then, there were usually some of the hands arriving who would help, and if time was tight, they could be left to do it on their own. If the grain to be threshed was different to the previous day, riddles would need to be changed and the volume of air adjusted.

When using the tier the procedure for opening the machine out was the same, but the tier was wound down to just below the working position and the driving chain was fitted to the sprockets. The tier was then wound up carefully to tension the chain, with an idler running in the slack chain on the top run. The farmer provided the twine, which was binder twine, and then the balls were placed in the band boxes and the twine connected to the lengths remaining from the previous day. It went through twine tensioners on the band box, through a guide under the tier, through spring tensioning arms and then around the needles and up to the retainers that held it in place.

It was then onto the tractor and set the machine running. If there was a minute to spare, with it running slowly, I'd have a walk round and check that everything was in order, and then at eight precisely, open the throttle and be ready to start. Very often the farmer would have taken such things as a selection of forks to the threshing site the day before. The men who were going to fork sheaves would select a suitable fork and, on a frosty morning, would go to the tractor and hold the fork shaft over the exhaust to melt any frost off it before beginning work. They would climb the ladder onto the machine and then pull it up behind them and set it on the machine deck to enable them to climb up onto the stack.

I very rarely did any lubrication first thing on a morning, but at ten o'clock time I had my drink and bite to eat as quickly as possible, and then spent five or ten minutes on greasing. On the machine the only daily greasing was top and bottom of the grain elevator and the bearings of the rotary screen brush. On the baler, the ram wheels needed daily greasing, whilst the main gear wheel bearings and big end pin had oil reservoirs that needed topping up daily. When using the Hornsby tier there was a considerable amount of lubrication needed. The packers all had grease nipples, as did some of the main bearings, but many of the lubrication points were oil holes, which included all the points on the knotters.

When looking at the machine from the front, on the left-hand side was a lever that operated a dog clutch, which engaged the drive. It required two hands to operate, one to remove a pin that secured it in the out position, whilst the other hand pulled the lever away from the machine. The tier worked in a very similar way to the binder, with packers compressing the straw against four compressor feet. There were two raised tongues in the floor of the tier, which when sufficient weight of material was on them, depressed and tripped the tying mechanism. In addition to that, two of the packers were linked to the trip mechanism so that if sufficient weight was applied to them that would also engage the tying cycle. The tier man, if he suspected that a batten was big enough, would push his fork into the forming batten, where he knew these tripping packers were, and so trigger the tying cycle.

There was a lever on the right hand-end that would also trip it, and this operated through a spring that could be adjusted to vary the batten size. In the tying cycle, the needles came in from behind, pressing the material forward, whilst at the same time the compressor feet were drawn back into the straw so that it was tied under maximum compression. That required considerable effort and the shaker belt, which drove the tier, needed to be in good condition and kept tight. The next sentence is not for the ears of health and safety officials, but it was quite common for that belt to come off the front pulley. The tier man, having first disengaged the dog clutch, could put the belt back on with the machine still running. It was more difficult to do after safety guards were fitted, as the belt always went off to the inside of the pulley, but with practice, it could be put back on without stopping the machine.

Threshing day hands, in this part of the world, were generally a mixture. Some would be 'borrowed hands', where neighbouring farmers had an agreement that when one threshed, the other would send a man, or himself, to be reciprocated when he himself threshed. There would very often be four or five such hands. On one farm where the farmer had four brothers – all farming in their own right – all would turn up on threshing days, like a sort of family reunion. In most villages, there were several men or women who were self-employed farm workers. They spent the winter months going to threshing days and at other times they would hoe turnips, clip sheep, fork hay or sheaves of corn, and in the autumn, help with potatoes. Some of these people, if asked, would bring one or two additional workers, and this was the usual mix of people on threshing days. It was quite common for two women to be employed as band cutters. Some of these women were out threshing most days in winter and became extremely good at their job. One such woman was from a neighbouring village and seemed to smoke continuously. One morning as she went to light a cigarette, the match broke in half and the burning end fell onto the dry material on top of the machine. Only some quick thinking by the feeder man and the other band cutter as they stamped on this fledgling fire averted what would have quickly become a serious incident.

When planning the work ahead for two or three sets there were some important issues to bear in mind. If there was a temptation to have two sets working close together, you had to avoid farms who borrowed hands with each other. We were caught out on one occasion threshing for farms A and B who we knew did not borrow hands, but we had failed to remember farmer C, who shared with both farmer A and farmer B. Other issues that had to be borne in mind and avoided were market days – Darlington on a Monday, Northallerton and Stockton on a Wednesday – and to some, hunting was a serious matter. The Hurworth Hunt met on a Tuesday and the Bedale on a Friday.

It could be dirty, dusty work, and in those days there were no such thing as dust masks or respirators. Some men wore goggles or a handkerchief over their nose and mouth, and one man used to wear a lady's nylon stocking over his head, bank robber-style.

It would be impossible to describe a day's threshing without mention of the R word. Whenever older characters are reminiscing about their experiences of threshing, rats would figure quite prominently. I would have to say that I am rather sceptical about some of the claims made: rats up trouser legs, up one leg and down the other, and so on and so forth, particularly as most men in those days wore leggings, anyway. What is certain is that rats were a prominent feature of threshing days. After all, it would be difficult to imagine a more perfect habitat for a rat than a corn stack, being warm and dry, and an endless supply of food. During the war, the Ministry of Agriculture saw rats as a genuine threat to the nation's food supply. Consequently, a law was introduced making it compulsory to erect a wire mesh fence around the threshing area. This legislation, to my knowledge, was never rescinded, but in peacetime it was very rarely adhered to.

In the 1950s, one of our sets was threshing at a farm where there was known to be a bad rat infestation, and a fence of chicken wire was in place around the site. We went to see them as they were finishing, only to find a pile of rats in the corner of the stack yard and one man counting the heap over. He counted 154. Had the wire not been there many of them would have escaped. There were often other stacks around or very often, a pile of wood in the stack yard. A rat's natural instinct is to try and escape by running away, but if cornered they will become aggressive. I once chased one into the base of a hollow tree. When he saw he was cornered he turned and began trying to bite my stick. It is not easy to swing a stick within a hollow tree but eventually I succeeded.

A couple of terrier dogs were the surest form of control, at one farm there were two border collies, beautiful dogs, and they were quite effective at catching rats but hadn't had the experience of some because at the end of the day, their faces were covered in blood where rats had bitten them. There was a very unfortunate occurrence one day when the farm's collie dog chased a rat under the front of the International pick-up baler. This was precisely the place where the crank arms came round. The rat escaped. I don't think I need say any more.

There would be two men on the stack forking sheaves. Sometimes, if threshing out of a shed and it was a long way to the back, a third forker would be employed to fork the back of the bay forward to the other forkers. There would be two band cutters – very often, but not always, women and the one feeder man on top of the machine. On the corn end there would be two or three men, depending on circumstances. If grain was being weighed in sacks, that took extra time. If threshing in the yard, it was very often carried to the granary on men's shoulders, in some cases with sacks left open so that the grain could be tipped out and the sack taken back for re-filling. If threshing out in the field, it could be loaded onto trailers and carted back to the buildings. If this was being done, three men would be needed; two would go back with the trailer, leaving just one at the machine to exchange sacks. There would be two or three at the straw end. If battening, the thresher man would watch the tier and fork battens behind him, and then somebody else would fork them onto the stack, where a further man stacked them. With the stationary baler, the thresher man usually put the needles through the baler and threaded two wires through the needle. Somebody else would then thread them back for the thresher man to tie them. With a pick up-baler, one man would be saved, so that with three on straw, three on corn, three on the machine and two on the stack, a total of eleven men would be required.

On top of the machine as the sheaves began to arrive, a row would be placed along the edge of the board with their buts out over. I preferred to leave these uncut, but others preferred them cut so that they could be picked up with a fork. Then the band cutters would allow a small heap of sheaves to build up in front of them so that they were not bending to pick sheaves up from near their feet. Each man on the stack forked to one band cutter. He placed the sheaves with heads in towards each other, the band cutter would then pick them up and pass them to the feeder so that the heads always went to the far side of the drum. The main reason for this was so that the feeder man did not get poked in the face with the butt ends of the sheaf. When feeding to a tier it was important that all heads were at the same side. This was less important when baling, and when a self-feeder was

being used, band cutters would very often place them the other way round.

Feeding was to some a repetitive and boring job. The essence was to open the sheaves out and present them to the drum as straight as possible. One morning when I was learning this job, I was feeding rather large wheat sheaves and opening them out and feeding a constant and steady stream of material into the drum. WO was needling the baler and he came up the ladder with a criticism: this continuous flow of straw out of the drum was hitting a curtain in the walker housing and being held there by the constant flow of straw. He knew this because the straw was coming into the baler in heaps. So I learnt from that, that it was better to essentially break the sheaf into two halves, with a slight delay between each half.

The other duty of the feeder man was to control the speed of the operation. At the start of the day, when forkers were forking downhill and were fully fit, and sheaves were arriving on the machine far too quickly, it was up to the feeder man to feed at the correct speed so as not to overload the riddles and the baler. This was less of a problem as the stack got lower and the men tired. Walter Robson had been a drum feeder in a previous employment, and had been taught that as each sheaf was fed to keep the last little bit in your hand. The purpose of this was that if there was a delay before the next sheaf, the drum would throw out grains that would pelt you in the face, and this small wisp of material would be held at arm's length to absorb these grains. Walter's problem was that as his arms went up for the next sheaf and he let this wisp go in such a way that it went into the drum head first at the far side of the drum. When he was feeding to the tier there would be a small quantity of straw coming endways into the head end of the batten, which would fall out as loose. As a consequence of this he went with the baling set as much as possible.

Band cutting was a matter of personal preference. Some would cut the band first and then pick the sheaf up. Others would pick the sheaf up and cut the band as they passed it to the feeder. One old chap would pick the sheaf up by inserting his knife blade under the string and carefully bringing it over to the feeder on the knife blade and then, by giving his wrist a jerk down and up, the string would be cut. It was important that the knife blades were sharp, and we carried a sharpening stone in the thresher tool box. It was important to be careful not to cut the feeder man's hand, but unfortunately, accidents did happen from time to time. As the day progressed, loose grain and straw built up around where the band cutters were working to such an extent that their feet became fastened down and it was almost impossible for them to move without clearing some of this material away.

The corn end was where many of the younger, fitter men preferred to be. It was generally cleaner and free from dust. In the time that I was involved with it, railway sacks had been abolished. Those were the ones that held 18 stone of wheat or 16 stone of barley, but there were 12-stone hire sacks, which in themselves required considerable effort. Until the last few years, grain for sale was always weighed at the thresher. A balance scale was most popular, with 4-stone weights and an empty sack on one side and the full sacks placed on the other side. There was usually a small scoop and a bigger bowl or container of some kind, so that the amount of grain in the sack could be adjusted until the scales balanced. Most farms had a sack lifter on which sacks could be placed, and by turning a handle could be lifted to shoulder height. Not everybody used them. If grain was loaded onto a trailer, a short piece of stick under the lower part of the sack would enable two men to quickly hoist it onto the trailer. One chap I knew who had carried corn in the steam era said he liked it best when threshing with a short belt, so that the engine front wheel was close to. They would them hoist the sack onto the wheel, which was the right height to get it onto his shoulders. On farms where the grain was needed for consumption on the farm it was usually carried up the steps into the granary. Some steps were wooden ones, inside the barn. They were not too bad, but some were old stone steps outside, covered in

The Davies baler new in July 1952 after being displayed at the Great Yorkshire show at Harrogate. WO borrowed a TVO Nuffield to travel the 40 miles to Harrogate to collect it.

moss, with no handrail, and they were extremely dangerous. It has to be said, however, that the experienced men managed very well and very few accidents occurred.

At the straw end, the thresher man was needling the baler. Balers had a strip of steel running along the top channel of the bale chamber, which was connected at its back end to a mechanism that stopped the feed of straw into the chamber. On this length of steel there was an adjustable triangular piece of steel that made contact with the needle stopping the conveyor. As the ram did not have a knife to cut the material as it entered the chamber, it was necessary to allow two or three strokes of the ram to completely clear the feed opening

before inserting the needle and then re-setting the feed trip. When Les was needling the baler he would re-set the trip first and then insert the needle. This saved one idle stroke of the ram, but it was important to know that the needle would go through first time. Les had sufficient confidence to know that it would. With the needle in place, two wires could be threaded through the grooves in the needles to reappear at the other side of the bale chamber, whilst at the same time, a man at the other side would thread the wires back through the other needle for them to be tied to complete a bale.

Various forms of tying wires were used. We always used a reef knot, but some twisted the wire ends together with

135½ 79 108½   33   16   33   109½   75   33⅝ 14½   141

47   7   6

27 THURSDAY (332-34)

G. Turnbull. EK.CK. FVN, T1.
     To 1 day threshing.   30 NOV 1952   8   10   -

M. H. Watson. EAJ. T2. B2, LH. JW.
     To 1 day threshing & baling.   30 NOV 1952   14   10   -

I. Bainbridge. JM. T3. WO. EM.
     To 1 day threshing.   30 NOV 1952   8   10   -

28 FRIDAY (333-33)
Removal Term (Scotland)

G. Turnbull. FVN, T1. (Ruffwell) B1. EK. CK.
     To 1 day threshing.   30 NOV 1952   8   10   -
     " ½ day baling.   30 NOV 1952   3   5   -

A. & C. Bainbridge. EAJ, T2. B2. LH. JW.
     To 1 day threshing & baling.   30 NOV 1952   14   10   -

I. Tyerman. JM. T3. WO. EM.
     To 1 day threshing.   30 NOV 1952   8   10   -

13 - 5 Shell Mex & B.P. Ltd. By 200 gs. gas Oile 1-3¼ 30 NOV 1952

An extract from the 1952 diary:

G. Turnbull had one day threshing with FVN, Fordson Major tractor, T1 was 34613 and Ernie and Chris Kirby where with it. M. H. Watson had one day threshing and baling with EAJ the Field Marshall. T2 34769 and B2 the Davies baler and Les Harker and Joe Walker where with it. I. Bainbridge had one day threshing with JMT3, the Model M tractor which is 35562 and WO and Eddie Makepeace where with it. On the Friday G. Turnbull had a second day, half of the straw was baled with B1, the Denning baler. T1 did not have a double drum pulley, so the farmers tractor drove the baler. A and C. Bainbridge had one day threshing and baling and T. Tyerman had one day threshing. We had a delivery of two hundred gallons of diesel for £13 - 5d.

pliers. Baling wire came in bundles weighing 4 stone, in varying lengths. Nine-foot, six was our preferred length, but 9 foot was acceptable, and we once had a consignment of 10-foot wire. There were just over 300 wires per bundle, making it possible to bale 150–160 bales from each bundle. It could either be bought with both ends plain or with one end with a preformed loop. We preferred the plain as there was a second option if the end became damaged, but in the latter years, only looped wire was available. One man could manage to carry the bale away and get back in time to thread the wires back, but at most places, two were available for that job.

If tying the straw in battens, three men were desirable because, in my experience, nobody ever brought out an elevator. At one farm, one day, they brought a trailer and reversed it under the tier for me to stand in to fork directly onto the stack. It was one of my worst days threshing; the dust was dreadful and being in a trailer with low sides, it was impossible to step to one side to get out of the dust. Another quite common practice as the stack was getting up high was to place a ladder beside it and for a man to stand part of the way up the ladder with his back to the stack. Then the man on the ground would pass him a fork that was already carrying a batten for him, and then to fork this batten the rest of the way onto the stack. If a pick-up baler was being used, at least one man would be saved. The following story probably illustrates why elevators were not generally used. At one farm, we were using the farmer's own baler, and in the afternoon, he placed his Lister bale elevator under the delivery plate of the baler so that nobody was needed on the ground. It conveyed the bales into a Dutch barn, where he himself was stacking them. All was going well but the chaps on the corn end thought he was having things far too easy. So to make his day a little more memorable, they dropped a sack of wheat onto the elevator for him to contend with.

It was sometimes necessary to clean off the top of the machine during the day – changing from one stack to another or a different variety of cereals, or at dinnertime, and at the end of the day. We carried a brush, a fork and a shovel on the machine for this purpose, and usually, the band cutters would help the feeder man with this task. After all the straw had been fed in, the man on the ground would go to the tractor and slow the revs down and then go back to the baler. As soon as he was satisfied

An extract from the 1956 diary:

There are now only two threshers, but much more of the straw is baled now. On the Monday W. Caine and son had one day threshing and baling with EAJ the Field Marshall. T1, 34769 and B1 is the Davies baler with Les Harker and Walter Robson. R. Alderson and son had one day threshing and baling with MAJ the Fordson Major diesel. T2, 35562 and B2 was the Welger baler, this was with WO and Eddie Robson. On the Thursday W. Caine and son had a second day and W. Harris had a day threshing with the Welger baler. On the Friday A. Rutherford had one day threshing and baling. J. A. Gill had two hours winch work, then in the afternoon G. W. Hogg had half a day threshing, using the tier.

20
Sun Rises 6.54
Sun Sets 5.33

FEBRUARY, 1956

Moon Rises 6.38 p.m. | 29 Days
Moon Sets 6.32 a.m. | 9th Week

26 SUNDAY—2nd in Lent (57-309)
○ Full Moon 1.41 a.m.

27 MONDAY (58-308)

	5		W. Caine & Son. To 1 day threshing & baling.	15	10	-
			LH. bonus ✓ EAJ. TI. BI. LH. WR.			
			R. Alderson & Son. To 1 day threshing & string baling.	16	-	-
			MAJ. T2. B2. WO ER.			

28 TUESDAY (59-307)

	5		W. Caine & Son. To 1 day threshing & baling.	15	10	-
			LH. bonus ✓ EAJ. TI. BI. LH. WR.			
			W. Harris. To 1 day threshing & baling. (string baler.)	16	-	-
			MAJ T2. B2. WO ER.			

29 WEDNESDAY (60-306)
Hare Hunting ends

E2	1/-					
	5		A. N. Rutherford. To 1 day threshing & baling.	15	10	-
			LH. bonus ✓ EAJ. TA. BI. LH. WR.			
			J. A. Gill. To 2 hrs. tractor, driver & winch	2	-	-
			MAJ. WO			
			G. W. Hogg. To ½ day threshing.	5	5	-
			MAJ. T2. WO. ER.			
			THN. ER. shifting & servicing B2 (AM)			

that all the straw had come through, he would knock the baler belt off and begin lapping up the baler. It would take some time for all the grain to leave the machine but when it had, it could be stopped and the belts rolled up and carried up the ladder to be stowed on top. At the same time, the feeder man was packing up the top of the machine and rolling the sheet out.

When everything was packed away and the ropes all tied, it was time to hitch the baler up and pull it out onto the road. We'd go back for the thresher, pull it out as well, and then reverse the baler to the machine and couple them together. They were then transported to the next farm. On arriving it was necessary to find out which stacks were to be threshed, and the new farmer might express a preference for which way round it was set. Once this was ascertained it was the business of setting. On occasions, with either a good level yard or dry field, it was possible to pull them in while still attached. More often, they were uncoupled, and the baler pulled in between the stacks and far enough forward to enable the thresher to be set.

There were several things to bear in mind when setting the thresher - firstly, equal distance from each stack, or if only one stack, parallel to it, leaving sufficient space to allow the scaffolding boards to be raised. The next thing was to make sure the drum was in the centre of the stack. This was important, otherwise one forker would have further to walk with his sheaves than the other one. Then came the levelling. The spirit-level on the back would be used for cross levelling. It was either a plank under the low wheel or, in a field, a hole could be dug for the high wheel. A spirit-level on the side gave you the end levelling and, in the case of a Marshall machine in wheat, they needed to have their heads slightly high, or as level as you could get them. This very often meant placing planks under the front wheels. At one farm where we threshed out of a Dutch barn in a yard with quite a slope, the back wheels had to be set on sleepers that were left protruding to the rear, and on which was laid the door for the sacks.

Setting didn't always go so smoothly. In wet ground conditions it became a job for the winch. On occasions, winching across several fields, I have also known it be so bad that the tractor would not push the baler back, in which case you had to go to the back of the machine and feed the winch rope under the thresher to pull the baler back. On one occasion, setting to two stacks either side of a cart road, the problem was that the ruts on this track were nearer to one stack than the other. The machine would not stay out of these ruts, which meant that the scaffolding doors could not have been raised on one side of the machine, and so a lot of digging and planking was necessary that night.

Threshing at Brick House Farm, Northallerton, early 1950's for James Sedgwick, standing talking to Mrs Elleray, his son Jimmy is looking into a sack of grain. The set is owned by Tommy Glasper who is feeding. Series 2 Field Marshall Ransomes thresher. The grain is being loaded into Doug Cragg's truck.

In some stack yards it was not possible to drive in with the tractor and thresher attached, as there may have been a building or wall across in front of the stacks. In this case, the machine was left as close and as straight as possible, then the tractor was unhitched and taken to the back of the machine, where the pushpole was connected from back of thresher to front hitch of tractor. The machine needed the drawbar lifting clear of the ground and hand-steering into position. Most makes of thresher had a steering lock; lengths of three-quarter rod fastened to the frame of the machine, then three or four links of chain at the front end, which fitted over hooks on the front axle. The point of

these was that if a front wheel came in contact with a brick or large stone, the axle would swing into full lock and the man holding the drawbar would not be able to hold it and could indeed be injured by it. All this had to be done in the dark, and we used to carry a torch to see the levels. I have seen men strike a match for that purpose but it was an extremely risky strategy.

The final operation was securing the machine so that driving belts could be tightened without it moving. The usual method was a wood chock behind and in front of a back wheel, followed by shear chocks. On a Marshall, there were steel brackets protruding from the frame above the front wheels, in the space between, wood wedges were hammered firmly in to make the machine rigid and stop any tendency to twist. On other machines, particularly on Fosters, wedges were driven in between axle support and main frame, again to stop twisting.

Threshing was charged for by the day, half-day or three-quarter day. Anything less than a half-day was not recognised. In 1942, when WO was not fully established, a contractor in the Richmond area lost his machine in a fire. The War Agricultural Committee approached him to know if he would take his machine to Richmond to be used by this other contractor with his traction engine. The reply was, "We will go to Richmond to thresh but not to use his engine." After all, the WD6 was only a few months old and he wasn't going to leave that standing to go and thresh with a traction engine, so they agreed to that. Some of the farms up there had been, and are now, all grass farms, but because of the compulsory ploughing out legislation during the war, they found themselves for the first time with some threshing. On one occasion they threshed at a farm in the village and

Ernest Crisp of Garmondsway Co Durham. Proud of his International B-414 tractor attached to a B-64 combine. He had however still managed to amass a good collection of corn stacks.

finished around two o'clock. The farmer wanted to pay and so they settled for a three-quarter day. They then moved along the village to a second farm and threshed there until 4.30 pm. Again, this man wanted to pay and was told it will have to be a half-day. A third farmer wanted his bit threshing and as it was September and nights were still light, they moved in and threshed it by 7.30 pm. He also wanted to pay and agreed to pay for a half-day. WO said afterwards that it was the only time he ever received one and three-quarter days' pay in one day.

Ernest Crisp (Grandfather's brother) farmed at Garmondsway, in Co Durham, some 30 miles away. In the International tractor days, WO threshed for him. He had quite a large farm and could arrange to thresh three and a half days at one visit. The usual practice was to travel up there on a weekend, usually Saturday afternoon, and thresh from Monday till Thursday lunchtime, then

Threshing and baling at Hill House Over Dinsdale 1963. The farmer, Reg Robson in the shirt sleeves at the corn end, sadly died within a year of this photograph being taken. Three o'clocks time, Walter and a band cutter are cleaning the machine top off. A shirtless Geoff Robinson and Bill Smith carry a sack to the pile. Reg's daughter, Anne, having brought the tea is now on the stack.

E A Martins threshing set from Great Ayton. Foster thresher and Series Two Field Marshall. With winch and home built cab.

travel back on the Thursday afternoon ready for a day near home on the Friday. Ernest had two four-wheel trailers with wood sides 4-5 feet high, probably designed for use with a 'green crop loader'. These opened from the middle, hinged on the corner posts. One day, whilst threshing away from the yard, they were using one of these trailers to cart sacks of wheat back to the buildings. They opened the front of one of these gates and lifted sacks into this trailer. Ernie was up in the trailer with sack barrow and was wheeling these sacks to the back of the trailer to start the load. Now there is a law of physics that states that when the weight placed behind the back axle of a trailer exceeds the weight of the body in front of the axle, then that trailer will tip up. Well, Ernie, having placed five sacks across the back of this trailer, was on his way with the sixth when it was shot up against the other sacks, and that law of physics was triggered. The pin through the turntable had no securing pin in the bottom so the body was able to rise, leaving the front axle on the ground. There was not a big overhang behind the back axle so the trailer went up to an angle in the region of 60 degrees. Ernie, having released his grip of the sack barrow, came head over heels over the sacks out of the trailer and ended up on his hands and knees on the ground behind the trailer.

It was generally assumed in the 1940s and 50s that the crop from 10 to 12 acres would constitute a day's threshing. With wheat yielding one ton per acre, or just slightly more, something in the order of 12 tons would be an average day's threshing. Similarly with the straw, when using the stationary baler, 150 to 200 bales would be normal. In the 1960s, with improving wheat yields, up to 20 tons of wheat per day became quite common. Some farmers set their binders to make quite large sheaves in an attempt to try and get more throughput from a day's threshing. With oats and barley, the sheaf forkers very often forked two sheaves at a time but with bigger wheat sheaves, one was all that most men could manage.

One day, threshing out of a Dutch barn in a stack yard, with the tier close to a brick building wall, a chap named Ronald, who worked on this farm, was forking straw. It was a warm day and very dusty. When the farmer came round to the straw end he enquired, "Are you getting it a bit rough, Ronald?"

"Rough," retorted Ronald, "I am about to burst out in hysterical laughter." Generally, farmers were very good and fair in the size of the day that they set, and as one said, "Nine times out of ten we would be finished threshing by four o'clock." Sometimes things didn't go according to plan and you ended up with a late finish and within reason, people didn't mind, and accepted it as part and parcel of the job.

Those of you involved in the vintage tractor scene will have come across the keen northern collector, Les Walker. In 1964, Les was the junior partner with his father Laurie, and on 23rd October 1964, I was booked for a day's threshing at their farm. We were to thresh oats from a bay in the shed, using their own B45 baler. Raymond Bramham and Brian Hall were on the corn end, and I fed the machine myself. It was a modern curved top shed, which would have held enough oats per bay for a three-quarter day's threshing. After we had been going for about an hour, Laurie went up into the next bay, which was also oats, and began forking across into the bay we were threshing in order to make it up to a full day. Nothing wrong with that; the trouble was, he went on too long.

After we came out from dinner (you could usually be out in little over half an hour, but it was customary to let the men have the full hour), one of the old hands came to me and said, "I think you want to be letting her go. We have just a fair afternoon in front of us." The word 'fair' in this context is a Yorkshire understatement for colossal. To be halfway down a bay one would expect to be level with the drum pulley, but on this occasion we were still above the boards. So, as I agreed with his sentiments, I went to the tractor and set the machine running. When I got to the ladder at the front of the machine, Laurie Walker was bent over greasing the baler knotters when Les arrived. "What's the matter with the bloody thing?" Les enquired.

A Foster machine hard at work. The machine on steel wheels, the small pulley above the front wheel is to drive a straw elevator, several more stacks are visible beyond the thresher.

"Ah can't get this nipple te tek grease," replied his father.

"Well, slap the bugger on anywhere, and let it find its own way in," was Les's reply.

It was indeed a big afternoon and we threshed on into the dark that night. You may be wondering how I can remember the date so accurately. Well, from that day to the end of its working life and beyond, that machine carried a message pencilled on its back boards that read, 'Bramham and Hall had one hell of a hard day 23rd October 1964.'

On one occasion in the early 1960s, we were threshing for a man by the name of Walter Clark. I was feeding when at about 9.30, a man in a suit appeared at the top of the ladder. He came over to me and asked if I was in charge of this operation, to which I replied that I was. He apparently was the local safety officer and he said, "This machine does not comply with current safety legislation and I have the power to order you to stop threshing, until such time as I am satisfied that all necessary guards are in place."

We had guarded most of the belts and a handrail around the top was in place. There were, however, some of the shaft ends protruding through the bearings that we hadn't covered, presumably regarding them as fairly low risk. But his biggest concern was the awner belt, which for part of its length ran behind the main driving belt, and we hadn't been able to design a satisfactory guard that did not foul the driving belt. I replied to him that he should talk to Mr Clark. I knew that Walter would not want to stop at that time of day with all the men employed for a full day.

About ten minutes later, the safety officer came back up onto the top of the machine and said, "I have spoken to Mr Clark and he is prepared to allow you to finish the day's work, but I must come and have a meeting with you before this machine is used again." This was obviously the topic of conversation at our next tea break. People were curious to know what had been said between the safety officer and Walter Clarke. Walter said, "Ah telt 'im te go to hell."

Two days later, we had our meeting with this official. He went around the machine making a list of all the infringements he could find. When we came to this awner belt, he had to concede that it was impractical to guard the whole of its length and agreed to a guard on the back pulley. During this discussion, WO said, "It's ridiculous to guard a belt which runs behind another belt," to which his reply was, "The last person who thought a guard was ridiculous appears in court next week."

Chapter 5

Steam Days

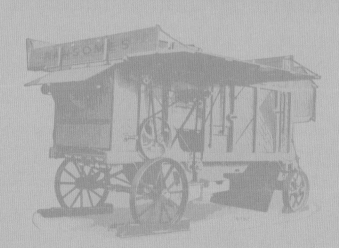

Souters Ransomes engine and wood framed thresher.

Threshing in this area in the 1920s and 30s was undertaken by J B Souter from Kirklevington, near Yarm. Souters were quite a large firm for that time, having many engines engaged in a variety of activities, of which threshing was only part of their work. There were varying reports as to how many threshing sets they actually ran; some suggested up to five, but I only have evidence of four drivers. Billy Harrison drove a Fowler, Percy Dabbs a single cylinder Ransomes, and the two best known to this area were a Ransomes compound, driven by Jack Shepherd, and a single cylinder Marshall, driven by Fred Storey.

Jack Shepherd had been born about 1880 and had become a traction engine driver at an early age. In 1914, he volunteered to join the Army. He passed the medical and was accepted. On being asked what his profession was, he proudly answered, "Traction engine driver". The recruiting officer was pleased to hear this, saying that that was what they were looking for. Jack was provided with an engine and baler, and spent the next four years baling hay to go to France to feed Army horses. After his demob he joined J B Souter as driver. The Ransomes engine was new in 1924, a compound, and was acknowledged among the other drivers as being the best of Souters' engines. It's not known how old the thresher was but it was also a Ransomes, giving him an all-Ransomes set.

Fred Storey, on the other hand, had an all-Marshall outfit – the Marshall single cylinder engine of similar age to the Ransomes, and wood-framed Marshall machine. Fred was a much younger man. He came originally from the Sunderland area, and he died in the late 1960s aged sixty-six years. In the years that I knew him he had poor lungs and was constantly out of breath, having spent too much of his life breathing in threshing dust.

The Marshall engine was notoriously slow on the road. One evening, there was a whist drive in Girsby School, and as people were going into the school they could hear Fred's engine pulling up Break House Bank at Eryholme. Some of the men attending the whist drive could tell by the sound of it which engine it was. As the crow flies, Breakhouse Bank is less than 2 miles away but because of a very large meander of the river, a detour of some 8 miles is required. Later, as the whist drive was turning out at around 10.00 pm, they were greeted by a fearful noise on the road, which turned out to be Fred and the Marshall engine still on his way to Dinsdale Grange.

Another story concerns Jack Shepherd threshing between two Dutch barns, again at Dinsdale Grange. On the ends of these barns were water tanks that collected rainwater from the roofs, set high enough to siphon into the tender on the engine. A hosepipe was placed in the top of the tank and down to the driving position on the engine. The driver had a cork, and when there was sufficient water in the engine's tank, he would put this cork in the end of the hosepipe. On this particular afternoon, Jack went up the ladder, having left the pipe-running to his feeder man, Tommy Leng, who was not familiar with this arrangement, and said to him, "A'll gi tha a spell, gan and mind that engine." About ten minutes later, Tommy, out of breath, appeared back on top of the machine he said to Jack, "Thoo'd better gan back te that engine, there's watter running out of er all ower."

One night, Jack was reversing the engine back to the thresher drawbar. When he stopped and looked down, his face was completely black; the only way you could see him was by his two white eyes peering at you. Tommy picked the drawbar up, but the engine was about 18 inches short. Tommy shouts up, "An 'inch'." Jack pulls on the lever, the engine gives one big chuff, jumps back into the thresher drawbar, Tommy drops the pin in and everybody was happy.

J B Souter gave up threshing in about 1940. Jack Shepherd worked for somebody else for a few years until his retirement and in retirement he worked part-time for WO as feeder man. WO learned a lot from Jack, a lot of which was passed down to me. This practice of tier man and feeder man swapping jobs for an hour or two in the afternoon

A county Durham threshing scene dated 1890. Included to show how little threshing machines changed from 1880 to 1950. This is a Ruston & Proctor machine, unusual because they did not have a shock crank. The oscillation was created by connecting rods driven from eccentrics on the shaker shaft. Hornsby single band tier, wood wheels and stacks built on stilts. The engine is by Aveling & Porter.

was a well established one. Although the man going into the feed box might be the owner of the set, when he was there the man on the ground was technically the boss. WO would say that when he was feeding to Jack, if everything was OK, you would not see him at all – he kept himself close to the sides or front of the machine. If, on the other hand, he went and stood out where you could see him, you knew that all was not well. He didn't need to shout or wave his arms, you just knew. One thing the feeder man was responsible for was making even battens of straw. With a double band tier you had to keep equal amounts of straw in both strings. One factor was that the machine

had to be absolutely level across the front, because straw could easily work its way across the machine as it travelled up the straw walkers. Another factor was that at the start of a corn stack, when the forkers were forking downhill, a pile of sheaves would build up on the boards that would encroach over the drum opening, creating a tendency to feed to the far side of the drum. We would sometimes place an uncut sheaf across the other end of the drum to prevent too much material going into the head string. That telepathy between feeder and tier man was something that only many years of experience can achieve. Jack died in about 1952.

George Turnbull's Aveling & Porter single cylinder engine engaged in road haulage work. Mr Turnbull is at the controls while Jack Baxter is steersman.

Fred Storey started threshing in his own business. By 1947, he had a new Ransomes machine, a Jones baler and a TVO E27N Fordson Major, which he used into the 1960s. In the later years, Fred, who never owned a car, didn't keep his own stock of baling wire, but came to us on his tractor and bought bundles off us when he was asked for threshing and baling.

There was another contractor in the Northallerton area called Jack Wood, who used a Model M Marshall and wood-framed Marshall machine. Jack Wood was a former steam man; he was also a good engineer. He had some specialised tools and equipment, and WO called on his services quite regularly. As a child I used to go in the van with him whenever possible. In Wood's yard there were no fewer than four traction engines. The one that Jack Wood had used was parked in a shed; the other three were outside in the yard. I believe that the engines in the yard were those of J B Souter. Certainly, the compound Ransomes was parked nearest to his house, and one of the others was a Marshall. I haven't been able to confirm what the other was, but it seems a reasonable assumption to believe they were Souter's as Jack Wood had bought them at the end of their working life. Then, on one occasion when we visited, all the engines had gone. Apparently, they had steamed and used one of the engines to pull the other three into the field behind the yard, and then all four

A rear view of George Turnbull's Aveling and Porter Engine, working in conjunction with his Ransomes thresher. This must have been a tea break as no men are visible. An indication as to how confined some stack yards could be with the engine standing through the gateway.

of them were cut up for scrap. This was about 1953, and within two years of that, the first traction engine rallies were being held.

A few miles to the west was a farmer/contractor by the name of George Turnbull. He threshed with an Aveling and Porter single-cylinder, which was used for many other duties and is shown whilst on haulage work. One morning, George went to thresh as normal, got the engine steamed up and the threshing under way and then said to one of his men, "I will have to leave you for an hour or two; you'll be able to manage." On getting their reassurance he left them. He first walked across fields down to the river, where he stripped off and jumped in the river and washed himself all over. He then, having previously positioned a bag with his best suit in, dressed himself in this suit

and went off to a nearby church. The purpose of all this was to get married, which was accomplished with as little fuss as was possible – no reception, no honeymoon, and back to the thresher in time to help lap up and move to the another farm for the next day.

There was a certain amount of resistance by the older engine drivers to change over to tractors. I would agree with them that when an engine is in good state of repair, with good boiler pressure and the governors functioning properly, it is a wonderful sound and a great spectacle. Some tractors were threshing as early as the 1920s, but the steam men could think up all kinds of reasons why they were not as good as engines, and kept them working for many years. Somebody was extolling the virtues of a tractor and thresher on pneumatics to Jack Shepherd one

Steam threshing in the East Riding of Yorkshire in 1940. The gentleman farmer is to the right of the group. The men are obviously posing for the photograph before tackling the basket of food on one mans arm.

day. "Pneumatics," exclaimed Jack, "we want nowt to do with pneumatics, we can't be sat by the road side at night mending punctures." The only experience Jack had had of pneumatic tyres at this time was on his bike.

WO was the first in this area to thresh with a tractor, in 1941. One night, he had set to a stack at a farm and on the way out he had to pass another farm at which contractor Jack Hall was busy setting in the stack yard. He stopped to talk to Jack, who asked how he was getting on threshing with a motor tractor. His concern was that a tractor on pneumatic tyres would not have sufficient traction for work in stack yards. WO replied, "Oh, you'd be surprised at where you can get with a tractor."

Jack's reply was, "With an outfit like mine you'd be surprised at where you can't get." He had a Foden engine and a heavy Ransomes machine on steel wheels that were notorious for cutting in and sinking into soft ground.

Other advantages to the tractor were that one man was saved, a tractor could stand and thresh all day unsupervised, and no coal or water were to be provided. So it was inevitable that by the end of the war, more and more were making the change, and by 1950, the steam engine had ceased threshing work.

Chapter 6

The Manufacturers

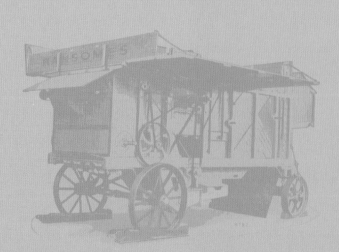

In the beginning there was the flail. Beating grain out of the ear with some form of stick had been the only way known and had been practised for centuries. Towards the end of the eighteenth century, mechanical means of removing grain from straw were being experimented with. First it was using wood bars on a rotary drum, turned by hand, rubbing against a series of fixed wood bars. The wood gave way to iron, and a horse wheel was developed to provide the power. Initially, that was all that the early threshers consisted of. Winnowing machines, for separating grain from chaff existed and were used as a separate operation from the threshing. Later, these two operations were combined into one machine. Various ways of removing loose grain from straw were tried, including a rotary rake arrangement over a large riddle, a reciprocating riddle, until finally what we now know as straw walkers were developed.

Early threshing machines were fixed in a barn that had a wheel shed built on the side, where horses walked around attached to a wheel that provided the power for the threshing machine. This would have represented a considerable investment for some of the small farms of the day. I cannot think of a farm in the 1950s that did not have a wheel shed, even well up the Dales into the Pennines and North Yorkshire Moors – all had their own wheel shed.

By the mid-nineteenth century, steam power was available. On large farms, stationary engines were located in a building to drive a length of shafting, from which belt drives were taken to various machines: mills, root cutters and a threshing machine. The next development was the portable steam engine, which was an engine on four wheels that could be moved from farm to farm with a team of horses. Threshing machines, which were now taking on the appearance of later machines, were similarly moved by horses. On level ground, four horses could move a thresher, but on slopes, six, eight or even ten were needed. For downward slopes, threshers were equipped with chokes, known as 'slippers', which were placed in front of the rear wheels. A pin was passed through it behind the wheel rim to prevent the wheel from turning so that the horses had to pull the machine downhill, sliding its wheels on the road. The next development was to use steam power to drive the wheels of the engine to move it along. This was to become known as the traction engine, which was able to move the threshing machines from farm to farm. By the end of the nineteenth century, threshers had developed to a stage where the only changes that occurred over the next

A Clayton & Shuttleworth machine clearly showing the Claytons distinctive diagonal frame members. Hornsby double band tier and self feeder. The Thackerays blowers can be clearly seen.

A Garvie machine at work in the 1960's. Fitted with safety guards, the elevator is positioned at the left hand side as was common on Scottish machines. The infill boarding is all horizontal with steel diagonal bracing.

sixty years were minor ones. In the early 1920s, steel-framed machines became available, and as tractors took over from traction engines, pneumatic tyres became more widely used.

In the days of the barn threshers, these machines were generally manufactured locally by joiners and millwrights. At the beginning of the steam era, it was the engine manufacturers who largely took up the challenge and made threshers as a way of promoting sales of their engines. Most prominent of these – and the three that would eventually dominate the English thresher market – were Ransomes, Marshall and Foster. The manufacturers were concentrated in the arable eastern counties: Ransomes, of Ipswich; Fosters, of Lincoln; and Marshalls, of Gainsborough. Others would include Clayton and Shuttleworth, Garrets and Robey, and Fisher Humphries, although the latter were not traction engine manufacturers. Ruston and Procter, of Lincoln, also made threshers and clover hullers. They amalgamated with trusser manufacturer Richard Hornsby, from Grantham, to

form Ruston and Hornsby, and in turn, they were taken over by Ransomes. The Scottish scene was catered for by Garvie, Crichton, Tullos and Barclay, Ross and Hutchinson. Most of the Scottish machines had their bottom riddles sloping the opposite way to the English ones, which meant that the elevator was at the left-hand side as opposed to the English right-hand side.

Most manufacturers used best quality oak for their main frames, filled in with tongue and grooved boards, and this continued till the end of production in the 1950s. Shoe connecting rods and the shoe supports, known as 'swingers', were made of straight ash. Ransomes offered Heavy, Medium and Light-framed machines; the main frame members on the heavy machines were 6 inches deep, 5½ on the mediums and 5 on the Lights.

Marshalls were the exception, making the first steel-framed machines in 1922, although these were produced in parallel to wood-framed ones, which continued up until the start of

The cast iron plate under he drum bearing of a Foster thresher. The image of a first world war tank is cast onto the plate. This was used on machines of inter war years. Post second world war machines did not have this.

the Second World War. From 1950 till the end of production, Marshalls used spring steel for their swingers. The steel-framed Marshall had side cladding of sheet metal, although the rear and top were tongue and grooved boards. Fisher Humphries also made a steel-framed machine, the backs of which were also clad in sheet steel. Robey used angle iron for its frame members but boards for its infill.

There is a Robey machine in the Lincolnshire Museum of Rural Life at Lincoln. Fosters of Lincoln had manufactured army tanks during the First World War, and on their threshers of the inter war period, the casting below the drum bearings had the image of a First World War tank cast onto it.

Henry Ford said of his Model T car, "You can have any colour you want so long as it's black." Well, with threshers, you could have any make you wanted but it would always be pink. Modern-day manufacturers would find this absolutely extraordinary that no matter what colour one painted one's other products, your threshers had to be pink. There were different shades of pink. For example, Marshall's were salmon pink, Fosters used snave, and so on, but all were recognisable as pink, this included the Scottish machines as well as the English. Wood-framed machines usually had the frame members and pulleys painted red. Axles and wheels would also be usually red. The early steel Marshalls had their angle iron frames and pulleys painted red. The 1944 machine did not have its frame members painted red, although the pulleys were. The 1947 machine had its pulleys painted pink, the same as the machine. The axles and fore-carriage were red but the wheels and drawbar were black. The steel Marshall carried one Britannia transfer, as used on the traction engines, situated on the left-hand side. The Ruston and Hornsby trusser was Oxford blue, similar to the E27N major.

English firms referred to their machines as 'thrashers', and although the Oxford Dictionary does recognise 'thrasher' as an alternative to 'thresher', I am sure that with an 'e' is the correct way of spelling it and the one that I would always use.

Before going through the various stages of the machine, you have to remember that when these machines were developed there were no selective weed killers, straw was considered almost as valuable as grain, and grain had to be dressed to the highest standard, which meant not only removing all chaff and short straw but also all weed seeds.

Machines were available in widths from 36 to 60 inches, with 54-inch being the most popular. There was an occasional 48-inch, but I have never seen a 36 or 60-inch model. Most drums were 22 inches in diameter, the exception being the Ransomes, which had a 24-inch drum. The correct speed for a 22-inch drum is 1,050rpm, and slightly slower for a 24-inch one.

In some parts of the country, notably Lincolnshire, there was a preference to transport the machines 'in reverse'. That is to say that the turntable and drawbar were located under the corn spouts. If towing a loose straw elevator or straw jack, then they would be in the correct order when setting to the stacks.

There were eight beater bars on a thresher drum running over a concave, as is the case with combines. The concave was in two sections; rods went through the machine behind the concave to adjusting bolts on the side of the machine. The bottom concave could be set close to the drum, both top and bottom, whilst the top one was left wider at the top to allow material to enter. When threshing beans, the bottom concave was adjusted back off the drum and the top rod was pulled out completely, allowing that concave to fall back well clear of the drum. For maintenance purposes, we changed beater bars after approximately 150 days threshing; the concaves would be pulled out and turned, to allow both sides of their bars to be used. After both sides were worn, it was possible to send them to specialist firms who would plane the bars of the concave, giving them another lease of life. This could happen several times. In fact, I cannot remember us ever buying new concaves.

On the Ransomes and Foster the shoe crank shaft was located behind the elevator; the belt driving the screen from this shaft is very short. The cranks had a much greater throw, the connecting rods were much longer to give more flexibility and the shoe wheel was much larger. This meant that the shoe had a slower and longer travel. The steel Marshall had its shoe crank shaft in front of the elevator and with a smaller shoe wheel so that its shoe ran faster with shorter travel. Most makes had three-bearing shoe crank shafts, the exception being the early steel Marshalls. In January 1947, WO collected 35562 from Gainsborough, and it had a two-bearing shaft, but he reported that the machines under

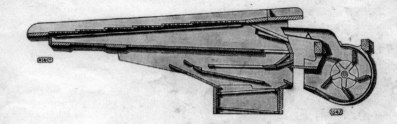

DIVIDED BLAST

All our Class "A" machines are now fitted with this arrangement, unless our customers order otherwise. From the illustration below it will be seen that a portion of the blast from the main blower is directed upwards through the caving riddle. The risk of choking is thus avoided, the cavings being kept alive whilst

passing over the riddle, and their clearance facilitated. Further, by means of this blast, any dust which might otherwise be carried down with the chaff, is taken away with the cavings. This divided blast passes through a spout in which a regulating valve is fitted. The valve is actuated from either side of the Thrasher by means of a quadrant, and the whole or any part of the blast can be shut off as desired.

9

Details of the Clayton divide blast as appeared in the Marshall sales literature.

construction in the factory all had three-bearing shafts. This machine subsequently broke its shoe crank and the replacement that was fitted was indeed a three-bearing one.

Most combines have disawner plates, which close off the first two or three spaces of the concave to prevent un-threshed heads getting through. Threshers did not have this facility. Barley had a characteristic known to the threshermen as 'necking', which meant that on first contact with the drum the head would break in half and the loose half would go un-threshed through the first openings of the concave. This half-head could not go through the shoe riddle and so it went out with the chaff. When chaff blowers were fitted, the blower threshed the half-head, the wind of the blower blew all the chaff away and you were left with a deposit of clean barley at the base of the chaff

heap. Farmers never failed to notice this. The cure was to open a narrow door between the feed box and drum and insert an uncut sheaf into it. This would sit on the top adjusting bar and effectively block off the top section of concave.

From the drum the straw would pass onto the straw walkers, known to thresher men as 'the shakers', four of them running on cranks that conveyed the straw out of the front of the machine. Marshalls offered a choice of length of straw walker – the short version, which was somewhat easier to mount a trusser to, or the longer version, which it was still possible to fit a trusser to and gave better separation of grain from straw, and it proved to be the most popular option. They were open-bottomed shakers that let any grain fall through onto an oscillating tray, which took it back onto the platform below the drum. The grain with chaff and short

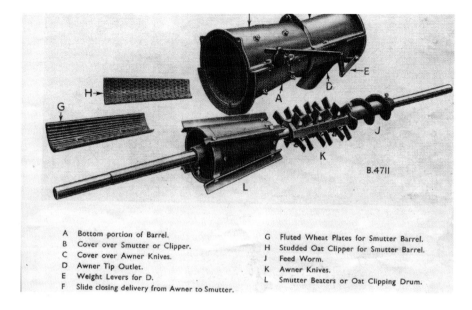

A	Bottom portion of Barrel.	G	Fluted Wheat Plates for Smutter Barrel.
B	Cover over Smutter or Clipper.	H	Studded Oat Clipper for Smutter Barrel.
C	Cover over Awner Knives.	J	Feed Worm.
D	Awner Tip Outlet.	K	Awner Knives.
E	Weight Levers for D.	L	Smutter Beaters or Oat Clipping Drum.
F	Slide closing delivery from Awner to Smutter.		

The Marshall Awner and Smutter taken from Marshall sales literature of the 1940's.

straws were then passed to the shoe riddle, the jack riddle and then the main bottom riddles before being elevated to the back riddles for final cleaning.

Clayton and Shuttleworth had made their own development of the main cleaning fan by creating two exits for the air coming from it. The top funnel of air was directed at the shoe riddle, which kept the shorts lifted and aerated to allow the grain to fall out more freely. The second blast of air came out below and was directed at the bottom riddles. Other makes with single blast separation blew the air through the bottom riddles first and whatever was left was directed up to the shoe riddle. In 1930, Marshall's bought the Clayton and Shuttleworth business and soon started to use the divided blast on their machines.

On the main cleaning riddles, the chaff was blown forward and out of the machine, while the clean grain after passing through two riddles was now on a bottom screen with very small holes, which grain would not pass through but weed seed would. If all this appears a bit elaborate, well it was, but at this time, grain was traded by the farmer going to his local town on market days with his sample bag of barley or wheat. Going into the corn exchange, there'd be half a dozen merchants or their representatives sitting at tables, who were only too ready to find fault with his sample. So quality of sample was important and threshing machine manufacturers made wild claims that their machines produced the best sample, very often with nothing to substantiate that claim.

The grain then fell into the elevator, which conveyed it to the top of the machine behind the drum. Combines

The fourth blast in the Marshall.

and American threshers separated clean grain from un-threshed heads and larger particles, which were then fed back through the drum. On European threshers this was not done. Instead, all the grain went on to the next stage of the separation process. Behind the drum was a device known as the awner, through which all the grain could be passed. The operator had the option to use it or not by moving a flap inside the machine by a handle on the outside. The awner was essentially a drum, with four angle iron bars running inside ribbed plates. The operator again had an adjustment as to how long the grain was held in the awner.

Grain then fell onto the back riddles, which were similar to but smaller than the bottom ones. These were flat perforated sheet steel with holes varying in size from one sixteenth of an inch in steps of a sixteenth up to three-quarters of an inch. A riddle box was located on the machine for carrying the spare riddles, which needed changing for different crops. Oats and beans needed the largest holes, while wheat and barley needed smaller ones. The one with the holes of a sixteenth of an inch would be placed at the bottom in each place, preventing grain going through but allowing weed seed to escape onto the ground. Again, there was a fan, usually located on the back of the machine, and the chaff that this removed was passed through an opening back to the platform under the drum. The grain then fell down to the rotary screen. On a Marshall there was the fourth blast, which simply blew air through falling grain. I found this to be particularly useful; you could adjust

The handle in place for adjusting the screen setting.

the volume of air with the right hand whilst holding the left hand under the spout where any removed material was falling. In the late stages of threshing after some fields had been harvested by combine, the wild oat problem became dramatically worse. This fourth blast could be set to remove wild oats, but you had to be careful not to remove too much light grain, and it would not remove every last wild oat but it was a useful contribution.

The rotary screen was the final component in this grain-cleaning process. The screen rotated very slowly, the grain was fed in at one end and progressed along it courtesy of auger-type flights within it. It was made of hoops of wire held in place by rods running longitudinally in it. It could be adjusted by fitting a screw handle to the

shaft end and rotating in whichever way was desired. This adjustment increased or decreased the space between the wires to allow split grains or any remaining weed seed to be removed. This was indeed a sample of grain fit to sow. In the 1950s we often hired out threshers, either with a man or without, to farmers who had a combine, but the sample of grain produced was so bad that it justified being dressed through a thresher.

The chaff that was blown off the bottom riddles landed in a trough that ran transversely across the machine, with a tilt flap in the bottom of it to enable the chaff to be deposited at either side of the machine. The shorts that fell off the shoe riddle simply fell onto the ground. A man, or very often a boy, would be given the job of raking chaff and shorts

The Marshall canvas type self feeder. The crank that operates the kicker bar can be seen as can the tines on the kicker bar.

clear of the machine. Some used a chaff sheet, which was a square section of hessian sacking that was laid out on the ground and chaff raked or forked onto it. When a suitable heap had been gathered the corners of the sheet were drawn together, and this bundle was hoisted onto one's back and carried off into a cattle yard or similar. Very often when raking shorts the thresher drawbar would be removed to make this job easier.

Mechanical ways of dealing with chaff and shorts were developed in the inter-war years. The main manufacturers offered a chaff bagging attachment, which was a small blower located usually on the right-hand end of the transverse trough, and which blew the chaff up a pipe into a hopper with spouts and sack holders at the bottom.

These devices were never popular in this part of the world, although they did feature widely in sales literature. They also developed and offered various designs of chaff blowers. Some had separate blowers for chaff and shorts with separate pipes blowing it well clear of the machinery, while others combined the two into one pipe. The pipes on the Ransomes blowers were carried on sheer legs some 3 feet above the ground. The Marshall ones used a much longer leg and were held some 10 feet off the ground, and then had a cyclone fitted at the end so that the chaff was dropped onto the heap rather than be blown into it. Our 1947 machine originally had the two separate blowers and pipes. The practice, when baling the straw, was to direct the shorts pipe above the baler to bale them up with the straw, until one day, the cyclone fell off, dropped into the baler and was baled up. The Marshall ones used either two pipes or a tray was fitted under the shoe riddle that took shorts back underneath to the transverse trough, where a larger blower was fitted to take both chaff and cavings (bits of straw).

There was a small firm in the Malton area of North Yorkshire by the name of J Thackeray & Sons, who manufactured a good combined chaff and shorts blower, which would be used on approximately ninety per cent of machines in this area. It consisted of a small blower on the left-hand side of the transverse trough, blowing chaff forward, round a bend and into a trough that ran across the front of the machine under the front of the shoe riddle. This trough collected the shorts, taking them into a much larger blower on the right-hand side of the machine. Under the blower the first pipe to be fitted was a ninety degree bend, which could be swivelled in any direction and allowed more pipes to be fitted along the ground.

Self-feeders were available from the 1920s onwards; most manufacturers offered a self-feeder as an optional extra. There were two basic types available: one was the drum type and the other relied on a canvass. The self-feeder was mounted directly above the drum, and the drive for it was taken from the back shaker shaft by a crossed belt that ran through a hole in the sill boards. The canvass was at an angle towards the front of the machine for the band cutters to place their sheaves. This transported it back towards the drum opening, where a kicker bar opened the sheaves out. This kicker bar was a mild steel bar, the width of the machine, with approximately six tines attached, which oscillated and opened out the sheaves.

The drum type self-feeder works in the same way as the canvass one. The canvass is replaced by a steel drum of about one foot in diameter with four rows of short tines around it. They take the material past a kicker bar before it enters the drum. The drum type is more compact. Nevertheless, the canvass one was more widely used. They did quite a reasonable job of opening sheaves out, but you were entirely dependent on the band cutters for placing the sheaves all the same way and laid straight across the machine. When the straw was being baled these considerations were less important, but battens produced from a self-fed machine could be of dubious quality. Obviously, the feeder man was not now needed, but that, in itself, created a problem, because from the contractor's point of view it became a one-man operation. Not only did that man have to open out and get ready on a morning but then had to lap up, yoke up and move in the evening. The year that we had a self-feeder, there was thresher, baler and portable tier to get coupled together for the move.

Sales of threshers were handled through agents, as happens with agricultural machinery today, the difference being that one firm could sell several different makes of machines. One such firm was the United Manufacturing Co, of Bury St Edmunds, who supplied threshing machinery and spares and supplies nationwide. Sheets, belting and baling wire were, of course, common to all makes of machines, but it is interesting to consider the comments that they made when selling one make against another. In 1945, they offered Davies or Ransomes balers with the comment that 'In our opinion they are the best balers made throughout Great Britain.' There was no attempt to say why, and no attempt to distinguish between the two.

They could supply any of the three major makes of thresher: the Ransomes comment was, 'The ideal machine for contractors catering for farmers who want the top price for their corn.' The Foster was 'The ideal machine for contractors threshing in a barley growing district.' The Marshall was 'The ideal machine for contractors catering for farmers in districts where Marshall machines are popular.' I don't know what basis they used for any of these statements but on the face of it, they do not appear to favour the Marshall.

New drum beater bars was the main area of expenditure. Belting, of course, was all flat belts, which the contractor carried rolls of, and this needed to

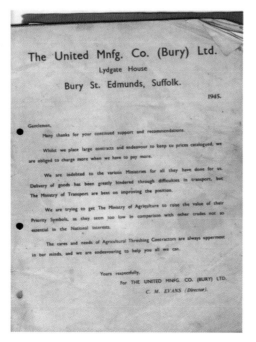

be cut to length and joined with belt fasteners. Various types were available. We preferred the Jackson fastener, which is essentially a piece of curved plate with two small bolts through it. Belts varied in width from 1½ inches to 3 inches, the narrowest, which drove the back blast, had one fastener, whilst the 2½ and 3-inch belts had two. A thresher man was able to repair belts on site, or if a belt was slipping badly, he would cut a small piece out of it and shorten it. In the tool box there was a selection of Jackson fasteners, a sharp knife, some spare belting and a stick of belt dressing. This was a stick of black resin, similar in size to a modern grease cartridge, which when held against a moving belt, would give a slight stickiness to it, preventing slipping. Swingers and shoe connecting rods were made of straight ash and could occasionally break. Connecting rods would first show a crack; they would run for some time with this crack but it was a warning to have a replacement ready. Swingers would break without warning, but if a length of chain could be found and secured in place, then the day's work could be finished.

There were four main manufacturers of trussers in England: Albion, Massey Harris, Howard, and probably the best of all, the Ruston and Hornsby. These machines were available in various forms, either single or double-band, and either mounted to the front of the thresher or portable, on wheels and drawbar. It seems to have been a regional consideration as to which one chose. In this particular area the mounted double-band was the preferred choice. Further north, in Northumberland and Scotland, the mounted single-band was preferred, while in the arable eastern counties to the south, very few tiers were mounted, and so if used, it would be the portable.

The tiers work very similar to a binder; there are a series of packers mounted on a crank shaft that compress the material into a batten. When it reaches the required density, which is adjustable, the tying mechanism is tripped and the needles bring the twine up to the knitters, where it is tied. The drive was taken by chain off the front straw walker shaft, and it was necessary to keep the straw walker belt in good condition, as considerable power was needed to compress battens.

Of the main three, Ransomes were the first to cease production in 1954, and the Ruston & Hornsby trusser production also ceased at that time. The Royal Show of 1956 was held at Newcastle-upon-Tyne, and I was taken to it as a school boy. There was a new Marshall and a new Foster machine there, but I believe this was the last appearance of an English thresher at a major agricultural show.

Scottish manufacturers may have gone on a little longer. Certainly, there was a Bisset Binder at the Smithfield Show until well into the 1960s.

Chapter 7
Threshers on the Road

Walter Walkington's threshing set of the late 1940's. Series 1 Field Marshall with homemade cab and lighting equipment, Ransomes thresher and Jones baler.

On some occasions threshing sets worked at one farm for two or three consecutive days, but on most occasions they had to be transported to the next farm on a daily basis, always in the evening, and set to the stack or stacks ready for the next day.

Threshing machines weighed between 5 and 6 tons, balers about 4, and these would be coupled together for transport and towed behind one tractor. This may seem like a trivial load to today's tractors but to the tractors of the 1940s, it was a considerable load with every hill or incline presenting a challenge. To get this in perspective, as today's tractors are approximately four times as powerful as those of the 1950s, it would be fair to say that an equivalent load behind a modern tractor would be two 20-ton trailers coupled together.

With all this night moving, machines had to be equipped with lights. In the Marshall tractor's day, one rear light was sufficient and we used ex-British Railways' oil lamps, which were secured to the rear of the machine. In those days we used fuel trailers that had 100-gallon tank of fuel, a box to carry oil and grease, and a board on which

The International WD6 tractor with some improvised headlights.

to carry a motorbike or pedal cycle. Thus the baling set consisted of tractor, baler, thresher and fuel trailer – a total of fourteen road wheels. When it was travelling past our depot it would pull up on the roadside, the driver would bring the tractor and fuel trailer in to the diesel tank to be filled, and while this was happening the two men would carry bundles of baling wire out onto hooks on the side of the baler.

By the mid 1950s, two rear lights were required, and as by now we were using Fordson Majors, the threshers were fitted with electric lights powered from the tractor. Balers also had lights fitted, and in the case of pick-up balers, we fitted a front side light on the extremity of the pick-up. One evening in 1961, WO was moving our International B55T pick-up baler when he had a collision with a young chap in a pre-war Morris Eight car. The chap said afterwards that he had been confused by all the lights coming towards him, and that was his excuse for running into the baler. The impact was tyre to tyre, which was enough to break the right-hand end of the car's axle from its moorings, with the result that the car spun round behind the baler and rolled onto its side. There appeared to be only superficial damage to the sheet metal on the baler, so it was taken into our workshop to be repaired because this machine needed to be in work by eight o'clock the following morning. Under the lights it was revealed that the gap between the

loops at the bale chamber end of the pick-up was twice as wide as it should have been, and on closer inspection we found that the baler axle had been bent by the collision. This meant that it was unfit for work the next day and so some frantic phone calls were needed to persuade the customers for the next few days to use the stationary baler instead.

By the late 1960s, we did not keep the thresher lights in best working order, as there was very little night moving needed. In the spring of 1967, I was drilling spring cereal seed and had a full program of work before me when a day's threshing had to be done. As we couldn't stop the drilling WO agreed to do this day's threshing. It was about 15 miles away, on a farm whose work we secured as other contractors ceased threshing. It was March; the clocks were still set to winter time so it was dark by six o'clock. It had been quite a late finish and with the first half of the journey being in a built-up area around the south side of Middlesbrough, so George the feeder man, who had his van with him, would follow close behind the machine to provide rear lights. This was probably highly illegal but it did make one feel a little more comfortable and that some gesture was being made to observe the laws of the highway.

I was home from my day's drilling when the telephone rang. It was George in a call-box reporting that he had sustained a puncture in his van. I enquired what

The Marshall brake lever. The near rope applies the brakes while the other one releases them. Part of the wire rope is visible behind the lever which goes to the back axle brakes.

he wanted me to do but he replied, "I can sort my puncture out, but it's him with the thresher; he doesn't know that I have stopped. He has kept going on." With that I got into one of our vans and set off to meet him. I didn't have far to go. The Nuffield had made good time and he had travelled about 10 miles with no lights at all. I turned in a driveway and tucked in behind the thresher and followed it back into our yard. WO climbed out of the tractor cab and walked back to the van, but was absolutely astonished to find it wasn't the same van as he had started out with.

"Where did you come from?" was his question, as he was totally oblivious to what had been going on around him.

Early threshers that had originally been fitted with steel wheels, converted to pneumatics by the use of lorry axles, were generally not fitted with brakes. Our 1947 machine, which came on pneumatics, was equipped with brakes on the rear axle. WO, who had previously had a bad experience with Dunlop tyres on a tractor, used to complain saying, "That new machine has come on Dunlop tyres, they will be no good, they will not last." In the late 1990s, I did some restoration work on that machine and at that time two of the original tyres were still on it. By this time they had become badly perished, and as I had some replacement tyres, I decided to change them. After removing the old tyres from the centres

I was able to pull the inner tubes out and found that they had their date of manufacture stamped on them. They were both stamped 09-46, and there were no patches or signs of repair on either tube. The conclusion I arrived at was that in fifty years, these tyres had not had a single puncture and had never been removed from their wheel centres. All this leaves a question mark over the advances in tyre technology over the last fifty years.

The brakes on the 1947 machine were operated by a rope, which was attached to the tractor where the driver could reach it. This, however, was not possible when the machine was attached to the back of the baler, so as we fitted brakes to the other machines in the 1950s, on the one that always went with the baler we fitted a handbrake lever at the back. On a hill, the feeder man – who was a passenger on the tractor – had to walk behind applying the brake as and when necessary.

Worsall Primary School was situated in a valley by the side of the road, the desks faced the road, but the windowsills were fairly high so you could not see cars going by, but you could see high vehicles. On one dreary afternoon I happened to look up and could see one of the thresher sheets. This was the baling set that had been into the Yarm area for a three-quarter day, and they were moving in the afternoon. Les Harker was the driver and he was waiting for his feeder man to walk past both machines and climb back aboard the tractor. At this point, my thoughts were interrupted by a great shout from the front of the room. I was ordered to go out to the front – something to do with not paying attention to what she had been saying. As I was making my way up the aisle, they were setting off outside. The tractor had run idle down the hill and then for a couple of minutes standing at the bottom, so when Les gave it full throttle for the hill climb it sent an enormous cloud of thick black smoke out, which blew across to and round the school windows. As I reached the front of the class the teacher bellowed, "What's making all that smoke out there?"
"Err, please Miss, it's … it's the Field Marshall, Miss."
Well, that was something akin to lighting the blue touch paper as she exploded. I cannot remember the entire tirade that followed but I do recall words such as 'insolent' and 'beyond all redemption' being used. The poor woman not only knew nothing, but wasn't prepared to learn.

One evening, Les was moving the set with the baler when the baler succumbed to a puncture in a rear wheel. He was able to stop a passing motorist who agreed to take a message back to our house. That meant loading the van up with all the jacks and puncture repair kit and travelling to where the stricken baler was parked. It was then a case of jacking up the baler, removing the wheel and repairing the puncture, and all that was then left to do was to inflate the tyre. We had a good foot pump, which was just as well because that was all that was available, so they started pumping, taking it in turns and periodically checking the pressure. This went on until it reached the required 75psi and all that remained was to refit the wheel. First one man tried to lift it, then a second joined in but try as they might, they could not move it. With it being laid on the grass verge, grass had become trapped between tyre and rim all the way around the wheel. It was absolutely fast to the ground. With a heavy heart, one of them unscrewed the valve and let the air out, which allowed it to be moved onto the road and re-inflated.

I have mentioned already the weight of this machinery in relation to the size of tractor used at that time, but try to imagine how much worse that would be when the road was covered in ice. In the years we are dealing with, from 1940 to 1970, global warming had not been thought of and there were some severe winters. Also, the winters that weren't deemed to be particularly severe still had periods when snow would lie for several weeks. There were two other factors that are difficult to comprehend today; one was that road salt was not generally available, and mechanical gritters had not come into use. The Council would come round

with grit in their lorries in summer and place heaps of grit by the roadside on hills and on corners. There were Council employees – who worked alone and were referred to as 'roadmen' – who came to work on their bike, with brush and shovel, and patrolled a length of road. This was a historic arrangement as they were originally employed to keep the roads clean of horse droppings, but they carried on after the horse days, spending their time in summer digging grips to let water off the road and generally tidying up the roadsides. When there was snow or ice on the road, they were meant to go to these grit heaps and spread grit on the road on corners and hills. Roads would get a covering of hard-packed snow, which could remain for several weeks and vehicles travelled on it. With care, it was reasonably safe. It became treacherous if there was sun during the day that melted the surface of this snow only for it to freeze late in the afternoon as the sun went down.

When we were using Fordson Major tractors, we very often used two tractors to move a thresher, usually one on the drawbar in front and one behind connected by pushpole.

We had a Patterson earth scoop that went on the three-point linkage of one tractor. The first operation was to find a Council chipping heap and reverse into it with this scoop and pick it up. The scoop lifted high enough for a thresher drawbar to pass underneath it, and we then had the benefit of some extra ballast on the tractor wheels and also, grit was to hand if needed. One evening, when moving up a hill with tractors fore and aft, both sets of wheels started to spin to a standstill and then they were not able to hold the machine on this hill. The whole outfit started sliding backwards down this slope, gathering speed as it went. The back tractor was not able to keep in line and the machine started to overtake that tractor until the pushpole made contact with thresher back wheel and tractor front. This brought it all to a stop but not before bending the pushpole and bursting the tractor tyre.

Up until 1954, WO rode a pedal cycle to go to thresh, which was carried on the front board of the fuel trailer. One evening, this bike was in the back of the tractor shed when somebody drove a tractor into the shed and failed to stop in time. The bike was badly bent to such an extent that the wheels would not go round, but WO made no attempt to replace it. Consequently, in the 1954/5 winter, Mother would go out in our Ford van and pick him up. It was a 1951 Ford Ten CWT van with no heater but, as all Ford goods vehicles were known at this time, its badge read 'Fordson'.

One evening, with snow on the ground, we were out in the garden playing in the snow and Les, with the baling set, was threshing only about half a mile from our yard. Our instructions were that as soon as we heard the Field Marshall pull out onto the road we had to tell Mother, which we did. We then got into the van and set off after him. Beyond the village of Appleton Wiske there is a hill known locally as 'Cheesecake'. It is not a steep hill but is a natural watershed, with rainwater falling on the south side draining into the river Wiske, then the Swale, and eventually the Humber, whilst that on the north side drains into ditches that make their way into the river Tees and out to sea at Middlesbrough. Well, on this particular evening, both sets had to travel up Cheesecake; WO was threshing in the Appleton Wiske area and Les was obviously going the same way.

We overtook Les before Appleton village but there was speculation as to whether we were in front of or behind the other machine. As we passed through the village, within sight of Cheesecake, Mother said, "There's your dad, and he's stuck." He was about one-third of the way up the hill and stationary. His feeder man had walked beside the machine with a wheel chock in his hand and as the Model M's wheels lost grip on the snow and spun to a standstill he was able to use the chocks to prevent the machine running back.

We hadn't long to wait before the unmistakable sound of the Field Marshall pulling its load through the village could be heard, and he was

All-Steel Frame Thrashing Machines

CLASS "S.M.L."

LIGHT TRACTOR TYPE

The light steel framed Marshall as used by Bill Turnbull. Note the absence of the fourth blast, they also had the shorter straw walkers. The pneumatic tyres were 5.00 x 2.

soon to the bottom of the hill. The tractor was uncoupled from the baler and driven up the hill. As it passed the model M, the Field Marshall's winch rope was attached to its front drawbar and he then continued to the top of the hill. There was a wide enough verge for the sprag (part of a threshing tractor winch that when lowered digs into the earth and prevents the tractor being pulled backwards by the winch rope) to dig into and the first machine was successfully brought up to the top. It was secured with wheel chocks as both tractors then went back down the bank to bring the other one up.

I was left beside this machine, and a torch was thrust into my hand with the instruction, "Don't let anybody run into that machine." Such responsibility. However, there wasn't a single car along the road all the time that this operation was going on.

Back at the bottom, the model M was attached to the baler drawbar, with the Field Marshall again preferred for winching. This time they were winching the full length of the hill and there wasn't sufficient winch rope for the whole length, so it was first pulled to the halfway point, secured, and then the second pull successfully brought thresher and baler to the top to stand beside the first machine. Each tractor was then coupled to its own machine, and they both set off and went their own ways.

In the war years, there was a man called Bill Turnbull, who threshed a round to the west of ours. He had a light steel Marshall machine and standard Fordson. This tractor was equipped with a Hesford winch and Opperman wheel strakes. One evening, Charlie (an uncle of mine) was with him as feeder man, and they had to go up Croft Bank. At Croft the road crosses the river and then climbs up the hill. This climb is made worse by the fact that the East Coast main railway line runs along the hill and so the road has a steeper climb to cross over the railway by bridge. There are houses all the way down both sides of the road, and there is a left-handed bend halfway up.

On reaching the bottom of this hill they decided to walk up it first to see what condition the surface was in. It had a layer of hard-packed snow about 3 inches thick. It had had some sun on it during the day, but now it was freezing hard. The road was totally treacherous and they would have had no chance of travelling up on rubber tyres, so Bill decided that they would open up the Opperman strakes. They then set off up this hill, and as Charlie put it, "She hobbled and hobbled on these strakes,

but we kept on going, round the bend and climbing onto the railway bridge, almost up and there was a clatter on the road behind." The drawbar pin had come out and the thresher drawbar was now down on the road.

"We're in a bit of bother now," said Charlie, as the machine set off backwards down this hill. And with these houses on both sides of the road and this bend coming up, there was sure to be a disaster. However, luck was kind to them because with the camber of the road, the machine veered to the nearside until the front wheel hit the kerb, and this forced the front axle into the square lock, where it came to rest.

As a footnote to that story, one's natural reaction would be that somebody had forgotten to put the lynch pin in the drawbar pin. Well, all the years that we threshed with Marshall and Fordson tractors, we never secured drawbar pins in that way. In fact, most pins did not have a hole in for a lynch pin to go through. It was only in the 1960s, when we were buying new Nuffields that came with a lynch pin on a length of chain attached to the drawbar pin, did we start using them.

And so to the events of Monday, 28th January 1952. Machine no 34613 had threshed at a farm called Viewley Hill, Worsall, on the previous Friday, but because of freezing weather was not moved until the Monday. Whichever way you travel from Worsall there are

A photograph that first appeared in the Northern Echo taken on 29th January 1952. The sheet and straw had all been cleared away by this time, the bent rear axle can be clearly seen.

banks. Chapel Bank is the steeper of the two but is relatively short and fairly straight. Worsall Bank, on the other hand, is not as steep but is fairly long, with bends, and for that machine to have taken that route would have added considerable distance. With the Model M Marshall doing 5 miles per hour, that was quite a consideration. On that Monday morning, I was off school poorly with cold or something of that nature. WO was pacing around, anxious to get the thresher moved because there was so much work booked up for it. He went to look at the bank, but was worried about it. However, by afternoon he was able to get an extra man and so he decided to attempt to move it. This other chap would drive the Fordson Major attached to the back of the machine by chain to act as brake for the machine on the hill.

As they were travelling from the farm a shower of sleet began to fall onto a thin covering of hard-packed snow. They reached the top of the bank and decided to proceed. I think that the thought of the tractor on the back would have given them a certain amount of confidence. As soon as they were onto the hill, the weight of the machine began to push the tractors, sliding their wheels on the road. WO had had a great deal of experience of handling threshers and one thing he knew was that in an over-run situation such as this, the machine would try and overtake the tractor. So as they gathered speed he tried weaving from side to side to keep in front of the machine. Despite his best efforts it did eventually beat him and the machine came past his left-hand side, which turned the tractor back up the hill. Because the machine was still attached to the tractor, it in turn was pulled across the hill. The combination of the slope of the hill and the sheer speed that they were doing at this time was too much for the top-heavy thresher and it rolled over onto its side. The Fordson on the back crashed into the back of the machine, smashing the corn spouts, its radiator grill and one headlamp bracket.

They then had to walk up the bank, turning a car around as they went, to a call-box in the village. I can remember that phone call coming to our house, Mother answering it, and asking if they were both alright. She then started what seemed like an endless number of phone calls, to the police, insurance and then the farms who were expecting a thresher that week, after which we were taken to grandparents for the evening.

The police had arrived at the scene of the accident and closed the road at the nearest junction. They sent for a heavy recovery vehicle – it was a Thornycroft mighty ANTAR, as used in army tank transportation. It was owned by British Road Services. In the 1940s, all road transport was nationalised and known as British Road Services. The 1951 Government began de-nationalising

it but the recovery service was still in government ownership. This vehicle stood on the road above the thresher and the wire rope was drawn out, passed over the machine and secured to the underneath drum pulley. As it began to pull at the machine it began to rise up off the road, but initially the back wheel laid flat on the road, resulting in the back axle becoming badly bent. Eventually, the wheel did leave the road but when the machine was upright again, that wheel, which was now on the low side of the machine, was bent in underneath. All this meant that, with the incline of the road compounded by this bent axle, the machine was standing at quite a severe angle.

In the interest of safety the police insisted that the recovery vehicle remain in place with its rope still attached. WO did not agree with this and said he thought the machine, although at a rakish angle, would have stood unaided. The drawbar of the thresher was swung round to face down the hill and a tractor was connected to it. It was now freezing and road conditions were atrocious, and once the tractor had moved a short distance its wheels would not hold on the road. The driver of the recovery truck was far too slow to release any rope and the tractor driver was helpless to do anything. Consequently, the machine was pulled over onto its other side. To use a modern-day expression, you couldn't have made it up.

It was now dark and it was felt unwise to attempt another recovery that evening, and so the rope was attached to the back axle and 34613 was unceremoniously dragged round to one side of the road, two oil lamps attached and it was left for the night.

The next day, road conditions improved. The recovery vehicle returned in the afternoon and the machine was pulled onto its wheels, this time bending the other side of the back axle. Otherwise, there were no further problems. It was towed to the top of the hill onto some waste ground, where it remained for

a couple of weeks until a replacement axle and drawbar could be found.

The insurance company wrote off that machine and WO was able to buy it back as salvage. A machine was hired for two weeks but by the end of February, a second-hand Marshall Machine, No. 34769 was bought as a replacement. The damage to 34613 was extensive. Nevertheless, by October of that year, it was threshing again.

The only thing to be thankful for in this whole sorry saga is that nobody was hurt.

Chapter 8
Threshing Day Meals

The kitchen range as fitted to most farm houses prior to the 1950's. This particular one was made by Blakeborough & Rhodes of Stockton On Tees. A large fire in the centre, oven to the left and hot water boiler to the right and a warm shelf above.

In the steam threshing era it was customary for the thresher men to arrive at the farm before seven o'clock in the morning, get the fire stoked on the engine, the machine opened out and ready for work, and then at 7.30 go into the farmhouse for breakfast. This would be a typical English breakfast of fried bacon and egg with thick slices of bread and a pot of tea. There would then be a mid-morning break at around ten o'clock, known as 'ten o'clocks', then back into the house at twelve for dinner. Afternoons varied from farm to farm. Some would send out 'three o'clocks' at three, followed by tea when the day was finished. Others would send out tea at four o'clock. Then after the steam men had moved to the next farm and set the machine, they would be asked into that house for supper.

When WO started threshing with a tractor in 1941, he went in for breakfast for one season only and then stopped that practice. It was traditional at that time and for some years after the war for farmers to keep a pig for their own use. In fact, it was encouraged by the wartime government, as part of 'Waste not want not'. It would be kept in a loosebox not too far away from the back door of the house, and it would be used as a kind of dustbin for all unwanted scraps from the kitchen. It would grow to be an enormous, obese animal before being slaughtered on the farm.

I have witnessed pig killing. When the day arrived for this animal to make the ultimate sacrifice, the local butcher was called, who first stunned the pig. For the one I witnessed, a small pistol was used. In earlier years somewhat cruder methods would be employed. There was a hammer in Grandfather's tool shed that had a shaft of about 3 feet long and the head consisted of a conventional hammer on one side, but the other side was formed into a form of pin of approximately three-quarters of an inch diameter by 3 inches long, which I was assured was for the purpose of stunning a pig. Its throat was cut and the blood that flowed was all collected in a bowl to be later turned into black pudding (an essential of this process was to keep the blood stirred). The most suitable device for this purpose appeared to be the human hand – Grandad's hand. He stuck to his job and when the blood had stopped flowing he picked the bowl up with one hand and carried it across the yard to the house, stirring all the time as he went. I don't know if this experience has had an influence on me, but I have never been able to convince myself that I might actually like black pudding.

With the aid of considerable amounts of hot water, the pig was then scraped to remove all the hairs from its skin, which seemed a painfully slow process. After one side had been done it was rolled over onto some clean straw so that the second side could have the same treatment. It was then dressed in the conventional way: a small quantity of it would be eaten as pork but as there were no refrigerators or freezers, the vast majority of it would be salted and cured for bacon and ham. A saying in this part of the world was that the only thing wasted when a pig was killed was its squeal. The head was boiled and the small amounts of meat on it, and in it, were made into brawn, or potted meat. The offal – heart, lungs, liver, kidneys, etc – all found their way onto the farmhouse table. Both my grandparents followed this practice until well into the 1950s. I remember my Northumbrian maternal grandfather cutting himself slices off a square block of almost pure fat with only a small strip of lean running through it. I said to him, "I don't know how you can eat that."

"Oh, he said, "it teks nee eatin at all man, it just slips straight doon."

Well, WO could not stand that extreme fat, and as he said, you got that every morning, which was probably behind his decision to stop having breakfasts.

At ten o'clock, a large basket and can of tea would be brought out to the stack yard, signalling a brief cessation in the activities. There was usually a sandwich of jam or cheese, a scone or teacake, and then a bun or cake of some kind. As much tea as you wanted, very often two cans – one sweetened and one not. At one farm in particular that I can remember the food was all wrapped in greaseproof paper, in individual portions. It was a welcome break lasting about fifteen minutes and there was always plenty of light-hearted chat that went on.

Dinner was normally eaten in the farmhouse. Towards the end of threshing days, a few people started to send the meal outside, but these were the exception. The traditional farmhouse had two kitchens – a back kitchen where the food was cooked and served, and a front kitchen that housed an enormous table, or two smaller ones, to seat up to twelve men. The layout of the farmhouse could have been dictated by threshing days, but in fact, many of them predated the threshing-day meals that we are concerned with here. The design of the farmhouse with its two kitchens came about because of the traditional large families of the nineteenth century, where up to ten children were quite common. This meant that with parents, children and possibly one or two helpers, there could be twelve people to be seated at mealtimes, or every mealtime became a threshing day.

In most of the houses, these kitchens were complete with a kitchen black-leaded range. These ranges dated back to Victorian days and were in regular use until after the Second World War. At the centre of the range was a fire, which was traditional, fuelled by coal or wood logs. On the right-hand side of the fire was a boiler, which held about two bucketfuls of water and had a large square lid on top. It had to be filled with buckets of cold water, and topped up by hand. The hot water was then taken out of the top with a ladle tin. On the left-hand side of the fire was the oven, with a space underneath to allow the fire to spread under the oven. I can recall going to a nearby wood to get 'oven sticks' in preparation for baking day. These were essentially logs of about 2 feet in length that could be pushed under the oven to get maximum heat to it. There was a hinged grid over the fire, which could be lifted to a vertical position to allow fuel to be added. On this grid would be placed the kettle, pans and even the flat irons for ironing clothes. There was a further such grid in front of the fire that was not as hot but was useful for simmering. Hinges and door catches were of stainless steel, while the rest of it was black, which needed to be kept clean and rubbed down with 'black lead' at regular intervals. Ranges were taken out in the years after the war and by 1960, had all but disappeared, to be replaced with Agas or other solid fuel cookers, and by the mid 1950s, electric cookers were appearing.

These kitchens had concrete floors at best; some had stone flags or brick type quarry tiles. There were often one or two clip mats, which would have been made by the farmer's wife from old discarded clothing. At the back door there was a stiff brush and a foot scraper. Everybody wore hobnail boots, many with leggings, and these were brushed off at the door before going into the house.

One thing that may seem strange was that we were never offered facilities to wash our hands. Most jobs, such as forking or handling sacks, one's hands kept reasonably clean, but when needling the baler with wires totally covered in oil, your hands were as black as the hobs of hell, as, of course, would be the engine drivers in the steam days.

Dinner was a very traditional English meal of stews, meat pies or in some cases, roasts, followed by a sweet course, which could be milk puddings of rice or semolina, fruit pies, steam puddings, such as chocolate, served with custard – all very high in calories that would be needed for the afternoon ahead. In the years that I was involved in this, food was plentiful and helpings were always generous. However, I understand that in the war years, with food on ration, that would not always be the case, and quite often, rabbit would be the main meat dish. At the farms where roasts were served there would be Yorkshire pudding, and as

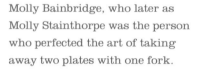

Molly Bainbridge, who later as Molly Stainthorpe was the person who perfected the art of taking away two plates with one fork.

Alice Bellerby, her young brother Keith and the farms sheep dog in the field. Alice, who later as Alice Strckland of Field House, Appleton Wiske, would serve her threshermen suet pudding with their dinners.

this is Yorkshire, it would be served first as a 'starter'. After the pudding was eaten the plates were taken out to the back kitchen, where the main course was served onto the same plate. You normally kept your knife and fork with you on the table, but at one house I can think of, when the lady took the plates two at a time, she took a fork on one of the plates so that on her return she knew which plate belonged to whom. At one farm the starter course was suet pudding. This consisted of a large enamel dish full of this suet pudding, which is essentially a dumpling mix, and each man took a spoonful and then added gravy. It was very welcome on a cold winter's day.

These were wonderful social occasions with light-hearted banter going on all the time, and you were able to keep informed as to what was going on in the local villages. Many of the older men had had a lifetime of working as a paid hand on threshing days. They had a simple, down to earth way of expressing themselves, they held nothing back and their honesty I found quite refreshing. One such character was a chap referred to as 'Old Ben'. In the time that I knew him he was an old aged pensioner but he continued to go out threshing because he liked it, although by this time he restricted himself to band cutting. Threshing one day for a man by the name of Horace Harrison whilst having ten o'clocks, Ben asked, "How

'Lowance time, as it was always called at a threshing day at Brockholme in 1942. Left to right: John Hugill, Arthur Foster, Clarrie (Clarence), Foster, Chistine Peacock, George Hugill, Mrs McAdam, Jeffrey Foster, Harold Garbutt. Kneeling: Alf Bowes and Robert Newcombe. Note threshing machine and half filled railway bag.

many bairns hest th now orris?"
"Nine," came the mumbled reply from Horace as he munched on his jam sandwich.
"Bye," retorted Ben, "what a lot."

We threshed at a farm on the 14th February one year, which is Candlemas day. It was a lovely day; the sun shone all day long and it was warm. At tea time, the younger ones among us were speculating as to how soon it would be before a start could be made on spring cultivations, to which the old farmer came out with:

If Candlemas day be sunny and fair
There's half the winter to come and mair.

And, of course, events were to prove him correct as it turned out to be a cold, wet spring with much spring barley having to be drilled in May.

One day at a farm where two of the neighbouring farmers were helping as borrowed hands, they both spoke with public school accents and their conversation was entirely concerned with fox hunting. They entirely dominated the conversation, with nobody else able to get a word in. It was a situation that called for an intervention by Old Ben. He said, "Ah se'ed a fox."

Olwyn Walker 1940-2001. Was a good tractor driver and an even better cook. Les is going to stack that wheat after he has finished posing.

A typical threshing tea break. This could be ten o'clocks or three o'clocks.
Mary Foster is the lady on the right of this group holding a butter basket while the tea
can stands in front of her. That style of can and basket were standard equipment for
threshing days. Half obscured by Mary a sack lift is visible.

"Really, Ben, and where was that?"
"Gaing down our village street."
"Well, how extraordinary. Tell me, Ben, did you happen to see where it went?"
"O aye, ah did, it went into the shop and bowt a paper to find out where the hounds were meeting next week."

On another occasion where there were known to be into the teens on cats, as we emerged from the house after dinner, all our plates were laid out along the path and licked absolutely spotlessly clean by these cats. One of the men went to a flower bed, picked up a handful of soil and scattered it along all of these plates. A young chap enquired, "What did you do that for?" "She'll have to wash 'em now," came the reply.

These were happy occasions and although we could not claim to have put the world to rights, we certainly identified many of its problems.

Joan Walker took a keen interest in all things agricultural including showing dairy cows. She could also apply a bandage to a feeder mans hand, after coming too close to a band cutters knife.

If there was three o'clocks, it was a very similar break to the ten o'clock one.

At tea time, sometimes in the house, but more often a basket of food and cans of tea were brought out into the yard or one of the farm buildings. There was always plenty to eat, with several sandwiches each, scones, pies and cakes – all home baked, of course. After a full day of hard manual work one could surprise oneself at how much food could be consumed. When threshing, there was no need to go to the pub in the evening to catch up on the local gossip and there was no need to go to the gym to work off excess calories.

Some of the farmers' wives did all this on their own but many were able to call on a helper. One farm we threshed at was run by an elderly couple and two of their sons. They had a married daughter who lived away and was a nurse in a local hospital. She had a day off on a Thursday and was prepared to come back home and help her mother.

It was quite a large farm with eight or ten days' threshing, and I can remember one of the sons calling to book the thresher very early in January and reserved every Thursday from then until March.

One exception to the home-baked food came at a farm we threshed at for several years during the mid 1960s. He had had a career in the Army, reaching the rank of major before retiring in his fifties and buying a farm on the banks of the river Tees. There had been two men employed on the farm with the previous owner and the Major kept them on to work the farm, or as he put it, "I am learning farming from my men." Neither he nor his wife had had any experience of farming and still less at feeding twelve hungry thresher men. When he came to see us, to ask about threshing, he had two days' of wheat stacked in a four-bay Dutch barn, and he enquired as to what would be expected by way of food. He said, "If I send out a whacking great pork pie and a can of tea, will that suffice?" He was assured that it would and so the arrangements went ahead. On the actual day, we threshed till eleven o'clock, when this large basket of pies and cans of tea appeared. The pies were served hot and were quite the largest pork pies that I had seen at that time; you certainly couldn't have eaten anything else. We then threshed on through the

normal dinnertime until, at two o'clock, the basket and cans reappeared, with exactly the same contents. We were on a two-stop strategy; it was different to the normal routine, but very acceptable nonetheless.

There was one large farm where they threshed, before my time, and they had almost sufficient staff for a day's threshing, and the only additional staff required were the two thresher men and two band cutter women. At tea time all the farm staff went home for their teas, leaving only four of them to go into the farmhouse for tea. They were shown through to a dining room with a fire roaring up the chimney and a Labrador asleep in front of it. A substantial tea was set out on the table, the centrepiece of which was a large plate of sandwiches, which on closer examination were found to contain thick slices of this afore mentioned home-cured fat ham. None of them were keen on so much fat and so they began opening the sandwiches and throwing the contents to this dog, who eagerly consumed it, and then eating the bread and butter. But as they were to find out, there is a limit to how much fat even a Labrador's stomach can take, when the contents of its stomach reappeared all over the fireside rug. Jack Shepherd, quick to apportion blame, turned to WO and said, "Now thoos dunnit."

Chapter 9

The Last Day

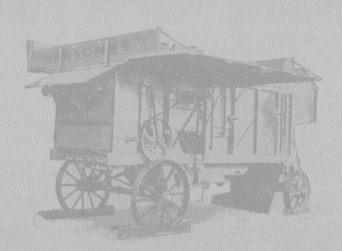

The demise of the threshing day was much more than just one piece of machinery being replaced by another, it was a whole way of life for many. It was a concept that had come into being in the nineteenth century and survived for a hundred years.

When other sections of industry close down, whether it be factory, coal mine or whatever, it often comes as a surprise and shock to many of the workforce. In the case of threshing days, it had been on the cards for fifty years; combines had been used in the USA and Australia since the 1920s. Up until the Second World War, they may not have been seen as a threat to the British threshing contractor, but from 1950 onwards, nobody was in any doubt as to what the final outcome would be.

The problem with the stationary threshing concept was that very little attempt had been made to improve productivity. From 1880 to the 1950s, threshing machines had hardly developed at all. Machines could probably have taken a greater throughput each day, or could have easily been developed to where they could have, but the limiting factor was manpower. With the whole of the crop from the previous harvest being manhandled many times over, both during the harvest and again on threshing days, it was the ability of a man to fork more sheaves, cut more bands, carry more grain, or stack more straw that was the limiting factor.

Chaff blowers had become widely used after the Second World War, a development that had saved one man. Self-feeders would also save a man, but they were not universally accepted. Those were the total of the advances made to threshing machines over a fifty-year period. In the late 1950s and early 1960s, I was a member of a local Young Farmers' Club, and on one evening, a progressive farmer gave us a talk on how he ran his farm. One thing he said was that "if you give a man a hand tool to work with …" i.e. a shovel or fork, "… then you have reduced that man to his lowest possible output." Towards the latter stages of threshing days I used to look round and think, there are ten of us here on our lowest possible output. We threshed for some arable farmers who were using combines for the vast majority of their harvest, but needed some straight straw for potato clamps. Two or three of those would place a box or tank under the corn spouts with an auger out of it delivering grain into a bulk trailer. These were very much a minority and livestock farmers preferred sacks to be carried up steps into the granary, right to the very end.

In this area the small to medium mixed farm predominated, and those farmers were growing cereals, mostly to feed to their livestock. In the years after the war, there appeared to be no alternative method of storing grain off the combine other than to dry it. Sealed stores and 'propcorn' did not become available until the late 1960s. Farmers with these relatively small acreages of cereals were reluctant to spend the not inconsiderable sums needed for a grain drier and associated equipment. For that reason, threshing days were prolonged for many years after combines had become widely used elsewhere. One can't help but compare this reluctance to invest with what had gone on 150 years earlier, when all the wheel sheds were being built and threshing equipment was bought by even the smallest farms.

In March 1970, we did a day's threshing using the tier, which we thought was our last day. When I got the machine home I packed some grease around the knotters and secured an extra piece of sheet over the front of the machine and around the tier. However, one year later, another farmer asked for two days' threshing and baling. This was totally unexpected. The baler was standing outside and the wooden top in the conveyer was fairly rotten, and we weren't sure if baling wire was still available.

However, wire was available and as we still had the thresher and baler, we agreed to do it, with the proviso that the machinery was pretty rough and may not be totally reliable. So off we went to do this final job and, in fact, the machinery performed reasonably well.

On the second afternoon, a lorry came to collect a load of this wheat. Up to the end of the 1950s, most grain was transported in sacks on flat lorries, but during the 1960s, bulk handling and bulk lorries gradually took over. So by 1971, very little grain was transported in sacks and this was indeed a bulk grain lorry – a six-wheeler carrying about 15 tons. An antiquated sack elevator was wheeled out to the side of this lorry, and planks were placed across the top of it on which the driver stood. So one man placed the sacks on the elevator and the lorry driver, knife in hand, balancing on these planks, cut open the sacks and let the grain fall into the lorry. Now how absurd had this job become? Two men working hard at the thresher bagging this wheat up, and two more working equally hard getting it back out again.

I have often been asked if I felt any emotion stopping the machine for the last time, wrapping belts up for the last time or the final sheeting-up. The answer to all that is no. We had had a hard day, and we had other work planned for the next day. The only concern was to get lapped-up as quickly as possible and onto the road home. We had about 15 miles to travel and we didn't want this job spilling over to the next day. There was no time to reflect on what a momentous day this had been and the fact that never again would we repeat it.

I have a photograph of number one son showing where his interests lay, taken in 1972. In the background is Ted Kirby's sheeted-up Ransomes thresher having completed its last day and, I believe, the last day of all, in this part of the world.

I did one or two demonstrations at working days after that but they never had the same atmosphere about them, and never will, because you can't turn back the clock. Agricultural contractors today are at their busiest during the summer months, threshing contractors, on the other hand, worked a season that ran from September through till April/May, and needed to seek alternative work and carry out maintenance work during the summer months. I can't think of another operation in farming that was so labour intensive, and I believe that the way neighbouring farms co-operated in the sharing of labour was unique. Threshing machinery is now the preserve of museums and collectors of vintage farm machinery. I believe that these machines should be preserved, representing as they do such an important part of agricultural heritage.